GRADE 5

Review, Practice, & Mastery of

COMMON CORE ENGLISH LANGUAGE ARTS STATE STANDARDS

Reviewers

Amy Barr • Park Hill School District • Park Hill, MO
Tracie Baumgartner • Valley View School District • Bolingbrook, IL
Barbara Burns • Lammersville Unified School District • Mountain House, CA
Karen Cooke • Cobb County School District • Marietta, GA
Amy Corr • Douglas County School District • Highlands Ranch, CO
Rachel Nichols • Lower Merion School District • Ardmore, PA
Arlene Peters • Orange County Public Schools • Orlando, FL
Brian Selling • Community Day Charter School • Lawrence, MA
Kim Sheehy • Sauquoit Valley Central Schools • Sauquoit, NY
Beverly Smith • Corona-Norco Unified School District • Ontario, CA
Colleen Thomas • Sandwich Public Schools • Sandwich, MA
Holly Walker • Whitman-Hanson Regional School District • Hanson, MA

1 2 3 4 5 6 EB 16 15 14 13 12

PP/Logan, Iowa, USA
1/12

35334
ISBN-10: 0-7891-8230-0
ISBN-13: 978-0-7891-8230-2

Printed in the United States of America

To the Student

This book will help you to review, practice, and master the English Language Arts Common Core State Standards. Here are the steps to follow to use this book.

1. Take the Tryout Test over Reading Literature, Reading Informational Text, and Language and then check your answers. Use the chart at the bottom of this page to find out your strengths and weaknesses in the areas covered. Remember the questions that are hard for you to answer. These will be the types of questions you need to work on the most.
2. Work through the units that follow the Tryout Test. The lessons in each unit review example items and provide a practice test based upon the standards. Fill in the Keeping Score chart on page 127 as you complete each practice test.
3. After completing all the lessons, take the Mastery Test. Your score on this test will show your understanding of the Common Core State Standards.
4. Work through the Writing Test Workshops section of the book. These lessons will help you learn how to read a writing prompt and how to get your ideas down on paper in a clear and organized manner.

Reading Literature	Tryout Test Items	Mastery Test Items
Unit One—Key Ideas and Details		
Lesson 1 Quote, Infer, and Summarize	1, 5, 6	1, 4, 5
Lesson 2 Character and Theme	3, 4	2, 3, 6, 7
Lesson 3 Comparing Elements in Literature	11, 12, 13	11, 12, 13
Unit Two—Craft and Structure		
Lesson 4 Word Choice	7, 8, 10, 14	10, 14, 15
Lesson 5 Poetry	15, 16, 17, 18	16, 17, 18
Reading Informational Text	**Tryout Test Items**	**Mastery Test Items**
Unit Three—Key Ideas and Details		
Lesson 6 Quote, Infer, and Summarize	19, 20, 22, 26	20, 29, 31
Lesson 7 Main Ideas and Supporting Details	21, 23, 27	21, 22, 23, 24
Unit Four—Craft and Structure		
Lesson 8 Using Multiple Texts	29, 30, 31, 35	25, 26, 27, 28
Lesson 9 Reasons and Evidence	32, 33, 34	19, 30, 32
Language	**Tryout Test Items**	**Mastery Test Items**
Unit Five—Grammar and Usage		
Lesson 10 Verbs	36, 40, 43	38, 42, 46
Lesson 11 Conjunctions, Prepositions, and Interjections	37, 38, 39, 44, 50	37, 41, 47, 48
Unit Six—Capitalization, Punctuation, and Spelling		
Lesson 12 Commas	41, 42, 48	39, 44, 45
Lesson 13 Titles and Spelling	45, 46, 47, 49	36, 40, 43
Unit Seven—Vocabulary		
Lesson 14 Word Meanings	9, 24	8, 9, 35, 51, 52
Lesson 15 Word Parts and Relationships	2, 25, 28	33, 34, 49, 50

Table of Contents

continued

Writing

Standards Key: RL = Reading Literature, RI = Reading Informational Text, L = Language, W = Writing

Note: A complete correlation of the Grade 5 Common Core State Standards can be found in the Grade 5 teacher guide.

This test will tell you how well you understand the Common Core State Standards **before** using this book.

Tryout Test: Part 1

Estimated time: 50 minutes

Directions: Read the following passage. Then answer the questions that follow.

The Frog and the Ox

One day a young frog came hop hop hopping back to the pond. His heart raced, and his eyes bulged in fright. "Father! Father!" he croaked. "I have seen the most terrifying monster!"

The young frog's father was sitting on a lily pad in the sun. Upon hearing his son's words, he quickly hopped over to the youngster. "What did you see?" he asked.

"Father, I saw a huge creature. It had horns on its head, a long swishy tail, and feet as hard as rock. It was ripping grass from the ground with its bare teeth!" The little frog shuddered.

The father frog chuckled. "Dear boy, you saw the farmer's ox, that's all. He's not so big, really. In fact, I'm quite sure that I'm nearly as big as he."

The young frog blinked in disbelief. "No, I don't think so," he said.

"Watch this," said the father frog. He puffed himself up so that his green chest rounded out. "How about that?" he asked.

"No, the creature was bigger," said the youngster.

The father frog puffed himself up even bigger. "I'm as big as he is now, right?"

"Not even close!" said the little frog. And a little giggle slipped out.

The father frog frowned. He gathered all his strength and sucked in as much air as he possibly could. Then he sucked in a little bit more. "How about—"

His words were cut short by a loud *POP!* The frog had puffed himself up so big that he exploded.

That day, the young frog learned that self-conceit can lead to self-destruction.

1 From this passage, we can infer that—

A it was a cold day.
B the young frog had never seen an ox.
C the father frog had never seen an ox.
D it was nighttime.

2 The prefix *dis-* used in the word *disbelief* means—

A under.
B over.
C after.
D not.

3 Why do you think the father frog responds to the young frog's description of the ox by puffing himself up?

A He is proud of the young frog's discovery.
B He wants to impress his son.
C He is scared of the ox.
D He wants to teach his son how to puff himself up.

4 Which of the following lines from the story states the theme?

A *The young frog's father was sitting on a lily pad in the sun.*
B *He's not so big, really.*
C . . . *I'm quite sure that I'm nearly as big as he.*
D . . . *self-conceit can lead to self-destruction.*

5 Do you think the young son was impressed by his father's behavior in the story? Why or why not? Support your answer with a direct quotation from the text. (3 points)

No, because the father was showing off to his son that he was bigger than a bull. The son was not impressed with his fathers behavior. No matter what the young frogs father did he was not bigger than the bull.

Directions: Read the passage and answer the questions that follow.

Paul Bunyan

Lumberjacks were big, strong men. But Paul Bunyan was the biggest and strongest of all. He was so big that he used a pine tree to comb his beard. He was so strong that he could drive a tree stump into the ground with his fist.

Of course, Paul was a lot smaller when he was a baby in Maine. But he was still bigger than any baby was supposed to be. In fact, some folks say that baby Paul's size got him thrown out of the state. It seems that baby Paul knocked down miles of trees every time he rolled over. Everyone wanted Paul out of Maine before he did some serious damage.

No one knows exactly where Paul and his family went next. But we do know that Paul showed up years later in Wisconsin. Or it might have been Minnesota. In those days, some states were completely covered with dark green forests. They were beautiful all right, but pioneers needed those trees to build houses, barns, wagons, bridges, and boats. So Paul decided to become a lumberjack.

Naturally, Paul was no ordinary lumberjack. There was the time that he dug a river. This happened in Minnesota for sure. Paul was cutting trees there, and he had to move them all the way to New Orleans. The easiest way to do that would be to float the logs south. But there was no river that went from Minnesota to New Orleans.

So Paul did some thinking. While he thought, he ate a snack. Nothing much. Just 3 hams, 10 loaves of bread, 150 pancakes, and 5 gallons of cider. But that gave Paul enough strength to dig. He dug the river that very afternoon. All the way from Minnesota to New Orleans. He called it the Mississippi.

As you can imagine, Paul's logging camps were big. The dining hall was so long that you couldn't see from one end to the other. And the food? Well, it took a lot of food to feed Paul and his crew. That's why Paul's blacksmith made a huge iron pot that held 1000 gallons of soup. The thing was so big that the cook had to use a rowboat when he made soup. He'd row out into the middle and dump in potatoes, cabbage, and meat.

Paul had himself a special friend too. He found his friend one cold winter while out for a walk. He hadn't gone far when he tripped over something in the snow. Well, Paul wondered what was there. After all, it had to be pretty big to trip him up. So he started digging through the snow. Before long he uncovered an ox—a blue ox!

It was easy to see that the ox was a baby. Still, it was half as big as Paul. So Paul carried the poor thing back to camp and named it Babe.

Babe kept on growing. He got so heavy that he left footprints in solid rock. But Babe's size came in handy. It didn't take Paul and his crew long to chop down all the trees in an area. Then they'd have to move on. But they didn't have to build a new logging camp. Paul would just hitch the buildings to Babe. Then the big blue ox would drag everything along with him. They cleared a lot of land that way too.

Then there was the time in Wisconsin where the road between the camp and the forest was very twisty. It was so twisty that men going to work met themselves coming back! It took the men far too long to get to work on such a twisty road. But Paul always had a trick up his sleeve. He hitched Babe up to one end of the road and then gave him a couple of tugs. Babe huffed and puffed once or twice. Then ping! That road snapped like a rubber band. Then it lay down nice and straight like a road should.

No one knows what happened to Paul and Babe. Some say they finished their work. Then they went into the woods to take a nap.

It could be that they're still there.

6 In a few sentences, summarize the story of how Paul dug the Mississippi. (3 points)

Paul Bunyan is the biggest and strongest lumberjack. When Paul was a baby, he rolled and knocked down trees. The people kicked him out of Maine. He moved to Wisconsis or Minnesota. He became a lumberjack There they need wood to build things. He cut trees He need to move wood to new Orleans. Mostly they float on logs, but no rivers. Paul thought. While he though he ate a snack (enough so people) The Same afternoon he dug the river from Minnesota to New orlean. This call Missisippi river.

7 What does the phrase Paul always had a trick up his sleeve mean?

A Paul liked to do magic tricks.
B Paul wasn't good at keeping secrets.
C Paul always wore long-sleeved shirts.
D Paul had a way to solve the problem.

8 An example of exaggeration in the story is Paul Bunyan—

A deciding to become a lumberjack.
B using a pine tree to comb his beard.
C going for a walk on a cold winter day.
D going into the woods to take a nap.

GO ON

Directions: Read the passage and answer the questions that follow.

All for a Little Food and Drink

1 As the hot California sun rose, Mesquite John woke up with a powerful hunger. He looked all around for something to eat, but the usual six dozen eggs and side of bacon for breakfast just didn't seem to be enough today. As he sat thinking about what to do, he heard a loud popping sound from nearby. Mesquite John walked over to investigate and discovered that the blazing sun was popping an entire cornfield. He quickly sprinkled a tub of butter and a bag of salt on an acre of popcorn and <u>dove into his breakfast</u>. Everything was going fine until Mesquite John started getting thirsty. In fact, his throat felt so dry that he began to cough. He coughed so hard that pretty soon he created a tremendous windstorm.

2 Mesquite John coughed his way across two states in search of water. When he reached the Great Salt Lake, he filled three huge buckets with salt water and quickly gulped them down. By the time he realized his mistake, Mesquite John was ten times thirstier than he was before. In his anger, he kicked the ground and made the Rocky Mountains get even higher. He leaped over the mountains in one big jump and headed for the Great Lakes. Mesquite John drank so much of that fresh, sweet water that the lakes were dry for a week.

9 Based upon the context, the word *investigate* means to—

A look at closely.
B heat up.
C create.
D grow.

10 The phrase dove into his breakfast implies that John ate—

A slowly.
B with energy.
C carefully.
D underwater.

Directions: Use both "Paul Bunyan" and "All for a Little Food and Drink" to answer the following questions.

11 Both Paul Bunyan and Mesquite John are examples of—

A realistic fiction.
B tall tales.
C fairy tales.
D myths.

12 The setting of both stories is—

A Salt Lake City.
B the United States.
C a land far, far away.
D Mexico.

13 How are the characters of Mesquite John and Paul Bunyan alike? Support your answer using examples from the text. (5 points)

GO ON

Directions: Read the following poem and answer the questions that follow.

Roses in Winter

Wild wind and wet rain lashed my face
As I slogged home from school.
Stepping in puddles that soaked my shoes,
Skidding in slick mud on sidewalks—
5 I'll tell you, it was no cakewalk.

Then there on the side of the path I saw
The bare, brittle skeletons of rosebushes.
In a flash, I was back in summer.

The roses bloomed lush and red,
10 Filling the air with nature's perfume,
Delighting the eye with splashes of color,
Soothing the mind with beauty.
I'll tell you, I was like a bee in clover.

Now as I pass by the brittle bushes
15 And think back to their summer state,
I can paint their beauty in my mind's eye.

I'll tell you, beauty is in the mind of the beholder.

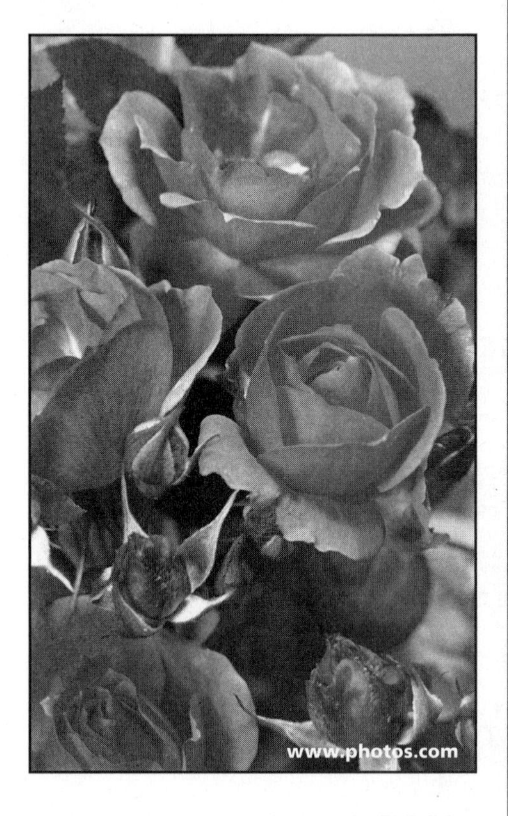

14 The poem's point of view helps us—

A understand the rosebush.
B picture the setting.
C understand the feelings of the speaker.
D understand the person who planted the rosebush.

15 In the first stanza the speaker feels—

A angry.
B glum.
C fearful.
D joyful.

16 In which stanza does the speaker describe how the roses appeared during the summer?

A stanza 1
B stanza 2
C stanza 3
D stanza 4

17 The phrase "I was like a bee in clover" means the speaker was—

A hungry for something sweet.
B angry.
C buzzing around.
D enjoying life.

18 Describe the theme of the poem. What lesson does the speaker learn? (3 points)

Take a break. Then go on to Part 2.

Tryout Test: Part 2

Estimated time: 50 minutes

Directions: Read the passage and answer the questions that follow.

Flo Jo: First Lady of Speed

People at the 1988 Olympic trials in Indianapolis, Indiana, could hardly believe their eyes. Who was the runner moving into position for the qualifying heat for the 100-meter dash?

This stunning woman had long, flowing, dark hair. The other runners wore plain shorts and tank tops. But this woman wore a colorful, one-legged bodysuit that shimmered in the sun. Most surprising of all, the runner had six-inch-long fingernails painted in a rainbow of colors.

Who was this runner with so much individual style? Her name was Florence Griffith Joyner. And she was about to prove that the way she dressed wasn't the only dramatic thing about her.

Making the Team

Florence Griffith was born in California in 1959. She always had a sense of style and individuality. And she loved to run. She even chased jackrabbits near her father's home in the Mojave Desert!

Griffith ran on track teams in both high school and college. Then she won a spot on the 1984 U.S. Olympic team.

The Olympics were held in Los Angeles, California, that year. Griffith won a silver medal in the 200-meter dash. Her time of 22.04 seconds was only 0.01 of a second away from the Olympic record.

A New Name and a New Mission

By the time the 1988 Olympic trials rolled around, Griffith had married track star Al Joyner. She was now known as Florence Griffith Joyner, or "Flo Jo" for short.

Despite the silver medal she won at the 1984 Olympics, most people didn't expect much from her in 1988. She was competing against many other track stars who were more famous. But Griffith Joyner was tired of being second best. She was determined to be number one in her field.

Running with the Wind

On July 16, 1988, at the Olympic trials, Griffith Joyner exploded out of the blocks. It was the qualifying heat in the 100-meter dash. Just a few seconds after the sprinters took off, Griffith Joyner was far ahead of everyone else. She crossed the finish line in just 10.60 seconds. The world record was 10.76 seconds. It seemed unbelievable that Griffith Joyner had beaten that record by such a wide margin.

The judges quickly determined that Griffith Joyner hadn't broken the record after all. The reason was the wind. If the wind is blowing behind the runners, they are able to move faster than usual. According to international rules, a record doesn't count if the wind is blowing more than 4.47 miles per hour.

The judges checked the wind-speed meter alongside the track. They discovered that the wind had been blowing more than 7 miles an hour. The wind had to be the explanation for her extraordinary time, people thought.

Two and a half hours later, Griffith Joyner and the other sprinters lined up for another qualifying heat. By now, the wind had died down and the meter at the edge of the track measured zero. If anyone set a record in this race, it would be official.

When the starting gun went off, Griffith Joyner burst out of the pack and took the lead immediately. She was well ahead of the rest of the runners when she dashed across the finish line. Her time was an astonishing 10.49 seconds—a new world record! And this time no one could credit the wind for Griffith Joyner's speed.

Olympic Gold

The 1988 Olympics began in September. They were held in Seoul, South Korea. Everyone was eager to see if Griffith Joyner could repeat her astonishing performance from the trials. She felt confident that she could.

When the starting gun sounded for the quarter finals of the 100-meter dash, Griffith Joyner burst out of the blocks and cruised into the lead. She crossed the finish line 10.62 seconds later, smiling from ear to ear. She was well ahead of everyone else on the track. And her time set a new Olympic record.

Griffith Joyner advanced to the finals, winning the gold medal with a time of 10.54 seconds. But because it was windy, this time wasn't recorded. Still, Griffith Joyner's record remains unbroken.

---

19 Based on details in the passage, you can infer that Flo Jo was—

A determined.
B lucky.
C boring.
D charitable.

20 Which statement BEST summarizes the section **Running with the Wind**?

A Griffith Joyner exploded out of the blocks at the 1988 Olympic trials.
B Griffith Joyner was far ahead of other runners during the first qualifying heat.
C The judges quickly determined that Griffith Joyner hadn't broken the world record.
D Griffith Joyner proved that the wind hadn't helped her break the world record.

21 Which detail supports the idea that people did not expect much from Flo Jo at the 1988 Olympic trials?

A She was tired of being second best.
B She was competing against runners who were more famous.
C She had won a silver medal at the 1984 Olympics.
D She had married a track star named Al Joyner.

22 Which detail does NOT belong in a brief summary of the passage?

A Florence Griffith won a silver medal at the 1984 Olympics.
B Griffith Joyner had both speed and a lot of individual style.
C The 1988 Olympics began in September.
D At the 1988 Olympic trials, Griffith Joyner broke a world record.

23 Which supporting detail best completes the web below?

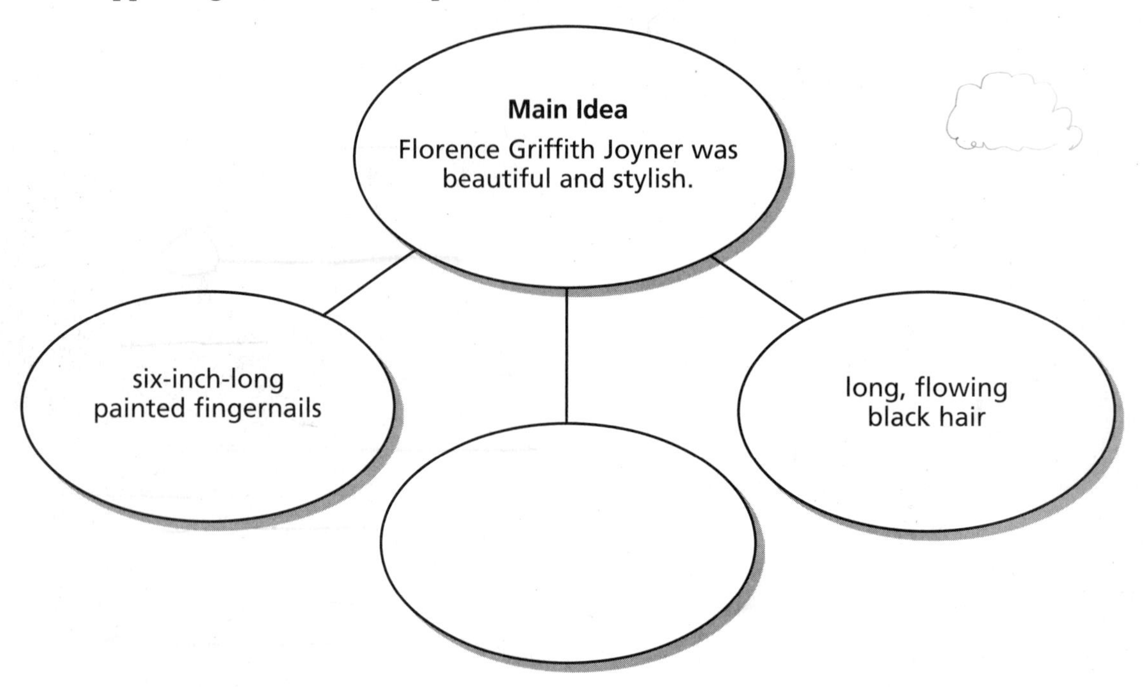

A married track star Al Joyner
B set many racing records
C holds the record for the fastest time in the women's 100-meter dash
D wore colorful, one-legged bodysuits

24 Read the dictionary entry for the word heat.

> **heat** (hēt) *n.* **1.** hotness; warmth **2.** feeling of strength, violence, or excitement **3.** pressure or criticism **4.** a trial run in a race

Which definition BEST fits the meaning of heat as it is used in the passage?

A definition 1
B definition 2
C definition 3
D definition 4

25 As used in the passage, a synonym for the word *stunning* is—

A sharp.
B nervous.
C beautiful.
D fast.

Directions: Read the passage and answer the questions that follow.

One for the Record Books

1 Basketball players have good games when they score 15 or 20 points, and excellent games when they score 25 or 30 points. Can you imagine one player scoring 100 points in a game? That's often more than an entire team gets!

2 This remarkable feat has occurred only once in the history of the National Basketball Association (NBA). The player who achieved it was Wilt Chamberlain.

3 Wilt Chamberlain was the most commanding player of the 1960s. He was also one of the tallest. Chamberlain was 7 feet, 1 inch tall and weighed 275 pounds. His great size, strength, and ability made him a huge basketball talent.

4 Chamberlain's reputation as a high scorer began in college. During his first game for the University of Kansas, he scored 52 points and grabbed 31 rebounds. Sportswriters and nonprofessional spectators alike recognized that in Chamberlain, a future basketball superstar was in the making.

5 After three years of playing college basketball, Chamberlain left school to join the Harlem Globetrotters. For the next year, Chamberlain traveled around the world with the team, becoming one of their stars. Everyone enjoyed watching the Globetrotters' outrageous ball handling and trick shots.

6 Chamberlain joined the Philadelphia Warriors of the NBA in 1959. In his first professional game, he scored 43 points. In his first season, he averaged 37.6 points a game.

7 Chamberlain started the 1961–1962 season with some remarkable performances. He scored 78 points in a triple-overtime game in December 1961, and in January 1962 scored an incredible 73 points during a regulation game. Those tallies gave him the top two single-game scoring records in the NBA. But they were nothing compared to what Chamberlain would achieve a few months later.

©Bettmann\CORBIS

Wilt Chamberlain

8 On March 2, 1962, the Philadelphia Warriors faced off against the New York Knicks. Chamberlain was on fire from the beginning, scoring 23 points in the first quarter. By the time the Warriors walked off the court at halftime, Chamberlain had accumulated 41 points. But he wasn't finished yet.

9 Chamberlain scored another 28 points during the third quarter. With just under eight minutes left in the game, he passed the 78-point record he had set back in December.

10 The fans were electrified by Chamberlain's performance. Suddenly, it seemed as if the impossible could happen. Chamberlain could score 100 points!

11 The entire crowd began to chant, "Give it to Wilt! Give it to Wilt!" Chamberlain's teammates did just that. They passed the ball to him every chance they could. And almost every time Chamberlain got the ball, he put it through the hoop.

12 Understandably, the Knicks didn't want anyone to score 100 points against them. So they did everything they could to keep the ball away from Chamberlain. When a Warrior got the ball, the Knicks immediately fouled that player. That meant that he couldn't pass the ball to the team's superstar.

13 When the Knicks had the ball, they held on to it for as long as they could. They didn't even try to score, because they knew the Warriors would grab the rebound and Chamberlain would get the ball that way.

14 When Chamberlain realized how hard the Knicks were trying to keep the ball away from him, he tried even harder to score. One way he did this was to make foul shots, or free shots given when a player from the other team breaks the rules.

15 Chamberlain was usually not a great foul shooter. His average was only 51 percent—that is, he made just over half the foul shots he took. But that night, Chamberlain made 28 out of 32 foul shots. This 88 percent success rate was quite remarkable.

16 Chamberlain's teammates also helped, by fouling the Knicks' players as often as possible. Whenever a Knick made a foul shot, the ball automatically went to the Warriors, giving Chamberlain another chance to score.

17 With just over one minute left in the game, Chamberlain made his 98th point of the night. He needed just one more basket.

18 The fans were as excited as they could be. But Chamberlain missed his next three shots. Would time run out before he could score again?

19 With less than a minute left, Chamberlain waited by the basket. The Warriors' Joe Ruklick got possession of the ball and flung it to Chamberlain. Chamberlain grabbed it and slammed it through the net. He had done it! He had scored 100 points!

20 Time-out had to be called because the fans ran onto the court in wild celebration. Chamberlain walked to the locker room with a huge grin on his face.

21 Five minutes later the court was cleared of fans, and the last 46 seconds of the game were played. The Warriors defeated the Knicks, 169 to 147. More than half of the Warriors' total points had been scored by just one player, Wilt Chamberlain.

26 On March 2, 1962, the Philadelphia Warriors faced off against the New York Knicks. How did Wilt Chamberlain's fans respond during this game? Use one quotation from the passage to support your answer. (3 points)

The fans were electrified. Wilt had done the impossible happened. "Wilt chamberlain scored 100 points- in 1. game.

27 Read this portion from an outline on "One for the Record Books."

> **II.** ______________________________
>
> **A.** Scored 52 points in first game at Kansas
> **B.** Important role on the Harlem Globetrotters
> **C.** 37.6-point scoring average first year in NBA

Which of the following is the main idea that belongs in the blank above?

A All-Time Basketball Records
B Poor Boy Does Well
C Wilt's Early Successes
D Speed and Strength

28 The term *regulation* used in paragraph 7 has to do with—

A sporting events.
B official rules.
C equipment.
D star basketball players.

Directions: Use both "Flo Jo: First Lady of Speed" and "One for the Record Books" to answer the following questions.

29 How were Florence Griffith Joyner and Wilt Chamberlain alike? Use details from BOTH passages to support your answer. (3 points)

Florence Griffith Joyner and Wilt Chamberlain are alike

____

____

____

____

____

GO ON

30 In both "Flo Jo: First Lady of Speed" and "One for the Record Books," the authors view the athletes' performances with—

A excitement.

B suspicion.

C jealousy.

D scorn.

31 Both Flo Jo and Wilt Chamberlain had unique appearances. How were they unique? Use details from BOTH passages to support your answer. (5 points)

Directions: Read the passage and answer the questions that follow.

Living Without Oil

by Alicia Carter

Oil is deadly to the environment. We should stop using it now. People argue that oil and oil products are important to the United States economy. They say that without oil, we would have to give up many things. There would be no more rubber tires, CDs, or two-liter soda bottles. These products are all made from petroleum. I say we should learn to live without these things.

Oil is dangerous to the environment. Oil tankers often have accidents, and the oil they carry spills all over the ocean. Animals can be seriously hurt or even die because of oil spills. The oil gets on the beaches and ruins them. It costs a lot of money to clean up an oil spill. If we stopped using oil, there would be no more oil spills, so our environment would be cleaner.

Some people might think they don't use very much oil. They might think that they only use oil when they drive their cars. The fact is, people use more oil than they think. Around the world, people use nearly 6000 products made from petroleum. Many of them can be found in your home. The carpet on your floor, the paint on your walls, and the plastic in your toys all probably contain oil. You might even be wearing oil because many fabrics have fibers that contain chemicals made from—you guessed it—oil! We must find substitutes for these products.

Americans use more than 25% of the oil that is produced in the world, but we produce only 13% of the world's total oil. At the rate we are using it, it is easy to see that someday we will run out of oil. What will we do then? We need to find different sources of energy now. If we wait until we run out of oil, everyone will suffer. There will be no way to heat our homes, and all our cars will be useless. We must act now!

The first thing we must do is reduce the amount of oil we use every day. There are some easy things we can do to do this. We should all ride bicycles, carpool, and take the bus instead of driving our cars. We can make sure we always wear clothing made of natural fibers such as cotton and wool. Some things are more difficult to do. For example, we should stop buying plastic products and rubber tires. Some people may think this is too difficult. However, we must do these things to save our environment. Let's all work together to save our Earth!

How Oil Forms

The recipe for making oil is fairly simple, but very time-consuming. Just mix the ingredients and wait for 10 million years or so!

Millions of years ago, the remains of ancient plants and animals fell to the bottom of the oceans. As time passed, the organisms decayed in the sedimentary layers of sand and rock. The organic material mixed with the sediment to form shale, or source rock. Over time, additional layers of sand and other sediment settled over the source rock. This resulted in intense heat and pressure on the source rock, which eventually caused the organic material to distill into crude oil and natural gas. The oil accumulated in porous rock such as limestone or sandstone.

32 Which of the following sentences BEST explains the writer's point of view?

A Products made from petroleum are important to our lifestyle.
B People should stop using oil because it is bad for the environment.
C Americans should look for more sources of oil so we can produce more.
D People should look for sources of energy other than oil.

33 Which of the following does NOT support the editorial's statement that oil is dangerous to the environment?

A Oil tankers often have accidents leaving oil spills in the ocean.
B Animals can be hurt or die because of oil spills.
C Oil spills can ruin beaches.
D Without oil there would be no rubber tires, CDs, or two-liter soda bottles.

34 What information in **How Oil Forms** supports the idea that we will someday run out of oil?

A It took millions of years for the oil we use today to form.
B It requires heat and pressure for oil to form.
C There are layers of rock that cover dead animal remains.
D Plant and animal remains were the original source of oil.

Directions: Read the following paragraph. Then answer question 35.

Most Americans support drilling for oil here in the United States, including drilling for oil offshore and taking oil out of oil shale. This is America's answer to our oil shortage problems. Supporting the oil industry will also mean more jobs for Americans.

35 Explain how the point of view of the paragraph differs from the one presented in "Living Without Oil." Support your answer with details from the passages. (3 points)

____

____

____

____

____

____

Take a break. Then go on to Part 3.

Tryout Test: Part 3

Estimated time: 15 minutes

Directions: Choose the best answer for the following questions.

36 Choose the correct verb tense for the following sentence.

When I climbed into the tree house, I ______ my friend Jamie.

A seen
B see
C saw
D will see

37 Identify the part of speech of the underlined word.

I found my dog <u>under</u> the bed.

A pronoun
B conjunction
C preposition
D interjection

38 Identify the part of speech of the underlined word.

<u>Ouch</u>! That really hurts!

A pronoun
B conjunction
C preposition
D interjection

39 Identify the part of speech of the underlined words.

<u>Both</u> DeShawn <u>and</u> Ming won awards for their artwork.

A nouns
B conjunctions
C prepositions
D interjections

40 Choose the correct verb tense for the following sentence.

In five years, I ______ in my house for ten years.

A will have lived
B live
C lived
D will live

GO ON

41 Which of the following sentences uses commas CORRECTLY?

A Please bring the following items to class: five pencils, one notebook, and a red pen.
B Mary, Jordyn Shaina and Oscar, came to my party.
C That's your friend Mandy isn't it?
D No I won't be at school tomorrow.

42 Which sentence is punctuated correctly?

A Janna said "Let's have a slumber party!"
B Janna said, Let's have a slumber party.
C Janna said, "Let's have a slumber party!"
D Janna said, "Let's have a slumber party"!

43 Choose the correct verb tense for the following sentence.

As I turned the corner, my bike ______ some gravel and I fell to the ground.

A hit
B hits
C will hit
D hitted

44 Read the paragraph.

> [1]Yesterday, Alissa and I took off our shoes. [2]We waded in the creek. [3]It was shallow, and the water only came up to our ankles. [4]While we were picking up stones, we spotted a fawn by the side of the water. [5]Then it saw us and scampered into the woods.

Which of the following BEST combines sentences 1 and 2?

A Yesterday, in the creek, Alissa and I took off our shoes.
B Yesterday, Alissa and I waded in the creek and took off our shoes.
C Yesterday, Alissa and I took off our shoes and waded in the creek.
D Yesterday, I took off my shoes and Alissa waded in the creek.

45 Complete the sentence below by choosing the correct spelling of the word.

No one can ______ the future.

A perdict
B predick
C predickt
D predict

46 In which sentence is the underlined word NOT spelled correctly?

A That bar is made of steel.
B She won a gold medal in the contest.
C I will pour some milk on my cereal.
D We saw a heard of sheep in the field.

47 Which of the following titles is NOT punctuated correctly?

A I just read the book *Every Thing On It* by Shel Silverstein.
B I really like the poem "Italian Food."
C I also like the book "The Giving Tree."
D Don't forget to read the chapter titled "Our Northern Neighbors."

48 Which of the following titles is punctuated correctly?

A Have you heard the song "Vincent" by Don McLean?
B It first appeared on the album "American Pie" in 1971.
C The song was inspired by Vincent van Gogh's painting, "Starry Night."
D You can read about Van Gogh in the book "Vincent's Colors."

49 In which of the following sentences is the underlined word spelled correctly?

A I through the ball to my dog, and he chased it.
B When you see the queen, you are supposed to bough.
C I road my bike to school today.
D Asia just read a book about a girl in Afghanistan.

50 Combine the following sentences into one sentence. Use the conjunction *either/or* in your new sentence. (1 point)

My mom will take me to the mall. My sister will take me to the mall.

____

____

____

Points Earned/Total = ______/70

Quote, Infer, and Summarize

Review the Standards (RL.5.1, RL.5.2)

- **Quote** a text accurately
- Make an **inference**
- Summarize the text

Q: How do I **quote** a text accurately?

A: When **quoting** part of a text, put the author's exact words in quotation marks. This helps the reader understand which words are directly from the text.

Example: In the poem "Sick," Peggy Ann McKay cannot go to school because she has "the measles and the mumps, A gash, a rash and purple bumps."

Q: How do I make an **inference**?

A: An **inference** is a reasonable guess. If a question asks you to make an inference, you combine what the text says with what you already know. For example, you may read a story in which the character is taking a test and working hard to finish before the bell rings. From this information, you can guess that the setting is in a classroom.

Q: How do I **summarize** a story?

A: A **summary** of a story should include the setting, or where the story takes place, the main characters, and the major events explained in chronological order. Do not include minor characters or events.

Try It

Read the following passage. Then answer the questions that follow.

A Find at the Flea Market

Along with her friend Amy, Jolene strolled past tables covered with sparkling jewelry and colorful china. She sailed past antique clocks and used books without even looking. While Amy stopped to admire some teacups, Jolene tapped her foot impatiently. Finally, she paused at the last table at the flea market. It was piled high with old catalogs and yellowing scrapbooks.

"Hmmmm," Jolene said. "This looks promising."

"This junk?" Amy asked. "You've got to be kidding."

"Maybe." Jolene smiled mysteriously. She gave Amy a dollar and sent her off to find lemonade. "Take your time and poke around," she advised Amy.

Once her friend was gone, Jolene concentrated on the scrapbooks. She leafed through them all, carefully examining the contents of each crumbling page. After looking with special interest at a scrapbook with a green leather cover, she casually asked the salesman how much it cost.

"Five dollars," he told her firmly.

Just then, Amy came back with two lemonades. "Five dollars!" she exclaimed. "You could buy a pair of earrings for that!"

Jolene quietly pulled her friend aside. "There's an envelope pasted inside that scrapbook," she whispered. "On that envelope is an 1893 Jefferson stamp that's worth at least $150."

1 How do you know that Jolene is looking for something special in the old scrapbooks? Use a direct quotation from the story in your answer. (3 points)

____

____

____

____

2 You can infer that Jolene sends Amy to get lemonade because Jolene—

A is extremely thirsty.

B wants to treat her friend.

C feels sorry for Amy.

D wants to look at the scrapbooks alone.

3 Which of the following is a minor detail and should not be included in a summary of the story?

A Amy and Jolene went to the flea market.

B Jolene was especially interested in the scrapbooks.

C The scrapbook had a green leather cover.

D Jolene found an expensive stamp inside the scrapbook.

Example 1 asks you to use a direct **quotation** as you answer a question. A good answer will answer the question completely and will also include a direct quotation that explains the answer.

Good: *Jolene is clearly looking for something in the old scrapbooks. The passage says that "Jolene concentrated on the scrapbooks. She leafed through them all, carefully examining the contents of each crumbling page." Then she looked "with special interest at a scrapbook with a green leather cover."*

A poor answer will not use a quotation from the story or will not use quotation marks to show which words are taken directly from the text.

Poor: *Jolene looked at the scrapbooks. She concentrated on the scrapbooks.*

Example 2 asks you to make an **inference**. When Jolene sends Amy to get lemonade, Jolene tells her to take her time. Then she concentrates on the scrapbooks. You can infer that Jolene *wants to look at the scrapbooks alone.* **Choice D** is correct.

Example 3 asks you to think about which choice is not an important detail of the story. Choices A, B, and D are important details of the story. **Choice C** is only a minor detail and should not be included in the summary.

Try It On Your Own

Directions: Read the selection. Then answer the questions that follow.

The New Kid

1 Tran's mother wandered into the living room and turned off the television. "You've been hanging around the house for the past week," she said. "Why don't you walk down to the park with me? You might meet some neighborhood kids."

2 "They aren't going to want some new person barging in," Tran answered. "I don't see why I can't just meet people when school starts."

3 "It's not going to be any easier then," his mother calmly replied. "It won't hurt you just to take a walk. If you don't feel like talking to anyone once you get there, we can turn around and come home."

4 Tran sighed. His mother always acted like there was nothing to worry about, even when there was. But maybe she was right. He wouldn't have to talk to anyone if he went to the park. Besides, it was boring staying at home all the time.

5 When they got to the park at the end of the street, Tran's mother sat down on a bench to read. "Come and tell me when you're ready to leave," she said.

6 Tran continued along one of the paths, hearing nothing but the sound of his shoes crunching on the gravel. There seemed to be no one around. He was somewhat relieved; if no one was there, he wouldn't have to meet anyone, and he wouldn't have to feel left out.

7 The path sloped down to a pond. On the bank, a boy about Tran's age tossed pebbles into the water. Tran ducked behind a tree where he could safely spy without being seen. "He doesn't look so tough," thought Tran. "In fact, he looks kind of sad."

8 Tran took a deep breath and walked toward the boy. "Hey," he called out with a forced smile, "I'm Tran."

9 The other boy looked up nervously. "Hi," he stuttered. "My name's Tony—I'm the new kid."

10 "Are you serious?" asked Tran. "I thought I was the new kid. We moved to town last week."

11 "I moved here from Minnesota about a month ago," said Tony with a grin. "I guess that means I'm not the new kid anymore—at least not the newest kid."

12 Tran grinned back. "Do you like basketball?" he asked. "Want to go to my house and shoot some hoops?"

4 From Tran's actions, we can infer that he is—

A excited to explore his new town.

B nervous about meeting new kids.

C ready to do schoolwork.

D angry at his mom for moving.

5 How does Tran feel when he first sees the boy on the bank? Include a direct quotation from the story in your answer. (3 points)

____

____

____

____

6 Which of the following details should NOT be included in a summary of the story?

A Tran is new to town.

B Tran's mother talked him into going to the park to possibly meet new kids.

C Tran's mother sat on the park bench.

D Tran met a new friend who had just moved into town as well.

7 Write a summary of the story. Be sure to include the main events. (3 points)

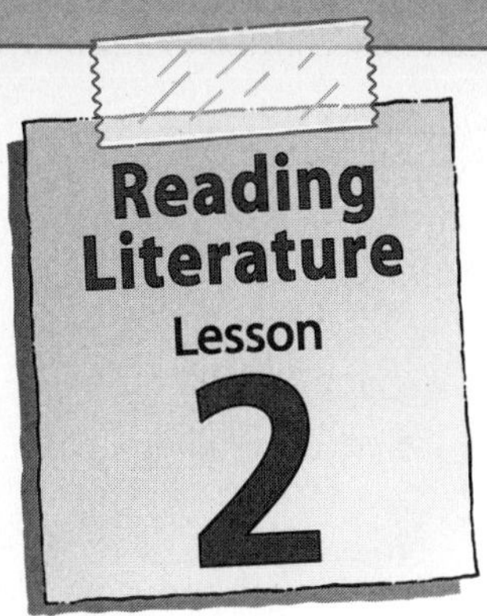

Character and Theme

Review the Standard (RL.5.2)

- Explain how **characters** respond to **challenges**
- Determine a **theme** of a story or poem

Q: How can I figure out how **characters** respond to **challenges**?

A: In most stories, the main **character** faces a **challenge** or problem. This is often called the *conflict*. Think about how the character must change in order to deal with the conflict. Consider how the character changes from the beginning to the end of the story. For example, a fearful character might become brave in order to save his brother from a burning house.

Character at the beginning: Fearful	→	**Challenge:** Brother is caught in burning house	→	**Character at the end:** Brave

Q: How do I find a **theme** of a story?

A: A **theme** of a story is the lesson about life that the main character learns. When reading literature, look at the conflict the character is facing. Consider how the conflict resolves. A good question to ask in order to find the theme is, *What does the character learn from the conflict she is facing?*

Try It

Directions: Read the following story and answer the questions that follow.

from Linnie's Letters

1 Elinore's family had decided to move west. They had heard lots of wonderful stories about life out west. People said that it had rich farmland, growing towns, and even gold. The family all agreed. Papa, Mama, and Elinore would ride in one wagon. Elinore's sister Phoebe would ride in another wagon with her husband, Robert.

2 But the trip had not been easy. Almost from the beginning, Phoebe and her husband, Robert, had troubles. Their wagon nearly tipped

over at a river crossing. One of their oxen broke a leg, and they ruined two wagon wheels.

3 Their wagon was simply too heavy for the journey. Now it was wobbling in a deep rut.

4 "You've got to lighten your load," the train leader ordered. "That piano is your problem."

5 Robert refused to leave the piano. He crossed his arms and would not budge. The wagon train leader said that they would leave him behind. "Let them go," Phoebe said. "Our family will travel on its own."

6 "No," said Papa firmly. "We should not try to cross this trail on our own. That would be foolish. The only answer is to lighten your load."

7 Robert took Phoebe by the hand. "Come, dear," he said quietly. "Help me stand our wagon upright."

8 Mama reached out and stopped Robert. "What do you plan to do?"

9 "We'll go back to the prairie town we just passed and make our home there," Robert replied as he turned and headed back to his wagon.

10 "But Robert," Mama said softly. "It's only a piano. Just leave it here and come with us."

11 "It is not only a piano," Robert said shortly.

12 Elinore watched as Robert led her dear sister, Phoebe, away. Three men from the wagon train helped them straighten their wagon. Within minutes, the wagon train continued its journey west. Elinore walked slowly behind her parents' covered wagon.

13 Up ahead, Mama and Papa faced forward, stubbornly, as they all moved up the steep hill, away from Robert and Phoebe.

14 Only Elinore looked back. Tears filled her brown eyes. She watched as Robert and her only sister turned and rode off in the opposite direction. Would she ever see her sister again?

1 What is a theme of this passage?

A Don't be a quitter.
B Making decisions can be difficult.
C Telling the truth is important.
D Friends support you through good times and bad.

2 Which event in the story helps the reader understand the theme?

A Papa, Mama, and Elinore ride together in one wagon.
B Robert decides that he won't leave his piano.
C Three men help straighten Robert and Phoebe's wagon.
D Elinore walks behind her parents' covered wagon.

3 How did Elinore feel about her sister staying behind?

A She feels happy for her sister.
B She is thankful because she was worried about the piano.
C She is angry that her sister would make such a terrible choice.
D She is sad and worried that she will never see her sister again.

In **Example 1**, you must identify the passage's **theme**. A story's theme reflects both the main idea and the meaning of the passage. Sometimes the theme is directly stated in the passage, but many times the author implies a theme through events or a character's actions. To identify a theme, think about the lesson about life the main character learns. In this passage, Robert has to make a tough decision between leaving the piano behind or leaving the others. The theme is that *Making decisions can be difficult.* **Choice B** is correct.

Example 2 tests your understanding of how the author develops the theme. You have already identified the theme of this passage as *Making decisions can be difficult.* Theme is often seen through the conflict faced by the main characters. In this story, Robert is conflicted about whether to go with the wagon train or keep his piano. It is Robert's decision to stay with his piano that communicates the theme. **Choice B** is correct.

In **Example 3**, we figure out how Elinore feels based on her actions. The passage states that Elinore looked back and had tears in her eyes. She also wondered if she would ever see her sister again. The correct answer is **choice D**, *She is sad and worried that she will never see her sister again.*

GO ON

Try It On Your Own

4 Describe how Mama and Papa respond to the fact that Robert and Phoebe will be staying behind. Use examples from the text. (3 points)

____

____

____

____

____

5 Which passage is LEAST helpful in figuring out the theme of the story?

A *But the trip had not been easy. Almost from the beginning, Phoebe and her husband, Robert, had troubles. Their wagon nearly tipped over at a river crossing. One of their oxen broke a leg, and they ruined two wagon wheels.*

B *Robert refused to leave the piano. He crossed his arms and would not budge. The wagon train leader said that they would leave him behind. "Let them go," Phoebe said. "Our family will travel on its own."*

C *Mama reached out and stopped Robert. "What do you plan to do?"*

D *Only Elinore looked back. Tears filled her brown eyes. She watched as Robert and her only sister turned and rode off in the opposite direction. Would she ever see her sister again?*

6 Elinore's response to being separated from her sister points to the theme that—

A things are more important than family.

B you must follow your dreams.

C change is difficult.

D you can't trust people.

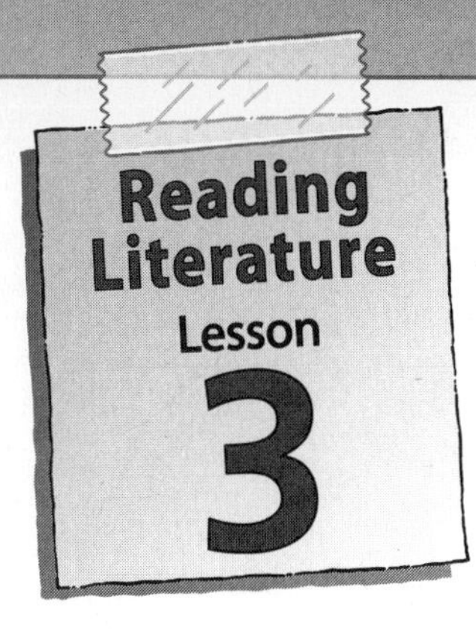

Comparing Elements in Literature

Review the Standards (RL.5.3, RL.5.9, L.3.b)

- **Compare** and **contrast** characters, setting, or events in a story or drama
- Compare and contrast themes and topics in stories from the same **genre**
- **Compare** and **contrast** English **dialects** used in stories, dramas, or poems.

Q: How do I **compare** and **contrast** elements in a story?

A: When you **compare**, you are thinking about how things are the same. Ask yourself: *How are these things alike?* When you **contrast** two stories, you are thinking about how they are different. Use a Venn diagram to help you understand how the characters, settings, or events in a story are similar or different. Use the following diagram to help you compare and contrast stories.

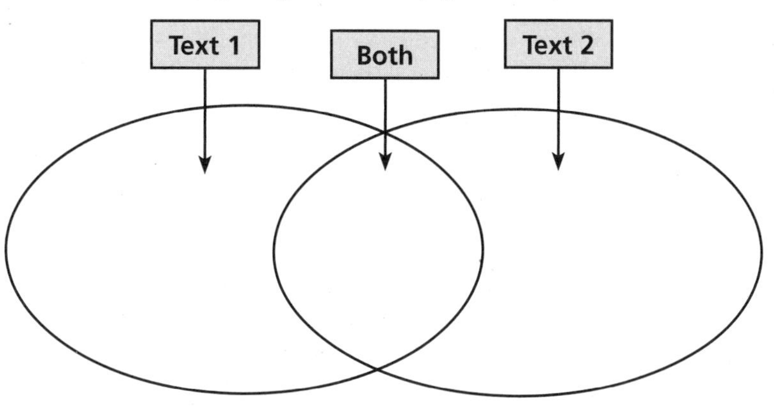

Q: How do I compare and contrast stories from the same **genre**?

A: A **genre** is a type of literature. You might think of it as a category the writing fits into. Some examples of genres include mystery stories, adventure stories, fairy tales, or haiku poetry. After reading two passages from the same genre, you may be asked to compare and contrast the themes or topics.

Q: What are English **dialects**?

A: A **dialect** is the unique way a person from a certain country or part of the country speaks. This might include slang or informal words such as *y'all* and *ain't.* If you see words like *thine* and *thou*, the writer is using a formal dialect. People from England use a different dialect than people from the American West. When you see unique words used by characters in a story, ask, *What kind of dialect is being used? How does the dialect help me understand the setting of the story?*

Try It

Directions: Read the passage. Then answer the questions that follow.

King Midas

In the age when gods ruled the earth, King Midas did a favor for the god Bacchus, so Bacchus offered Midas his choice of a reward, whatever he might wish. Midas thought for a moment and said, "I wish that everything I touch should be changed into gold."

Bacchus consented, though he was sorry that Midas had not made a better choice. Midas went on his way, rejoicing in his newly acquired power that he hastened to put to the test. He could scarce believe his eyes when he found a twig of an oak, which he plucked from the branch, became gold in his hand. He took up a stone; it changed to gold. He touched a blade of grass; it did the same. His joy knew no bounds, and as soon as he got home, he ordered the servants to set a splendid repast on the table. Then he found, to his dismay, that when he touched bread, it hardened in his hand; when he put a morsel to his lips, it defied his teeth.

Midas strove to divest himself of his power; he hated the gift he had lately coveted. But all in vain; starvation seemed to await him. He raised his arms, all shining with gold, crying out to Bacchus.

"Please," he begged, "deliver me from this glittering destruction!"

Bacchus heard and consented. "Go," said Bacchus, "to the source of the River Pactolus, plunge into the purifying water, and wash away your fault and its punishment."

Midas immediately followed the god's orders. As soon as he touched the waters, the gold-creating power was given to the river. And the sands of the River Pactolus turned to gold, as they remain to this day.

The Miser and His Gold

Once upon a time many years ago, there lived a man who loved his money. He loved it so much that he never spent a penny unless he absolutely had to.

The people who lived in his village called him The Miser. This was because he was so greedy for gold coins. All he ever wanted to do was look at his money. He loved to count it and just hold the gold in his hands.

One day, afraid that someone might try to steal his money, he decided to bury it at the base of a tree in his garden.

The next morning, he missed his gold coins, so he returned to the spot. He dug the money up and counted it all over again. Then he buried it again. This went on for many years. The Miser was so pleased that he had found such a good hiding place for his gold.

It all changed one morning. The Miser was counting up his coins as usual. He was so busy that he did not see the robber behind the tree who was watching him! As soon as The Miser had buried his coins and left the garden, the robber dug them up and ran away.

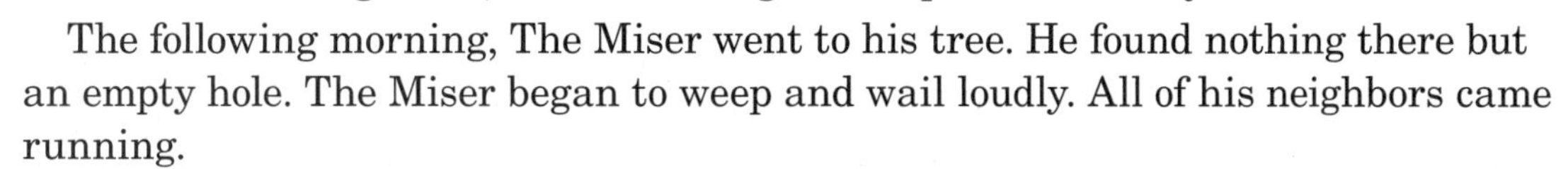

The following morning, The Miser went to his tree. He found nothing there but an empty hole. The Miser began to weep and wail loudly. All of his neighbors came running.

"Dagnabbit! My gold coins 're gone!" he cried. "I buried 'em here to keep 'em safe, and now someone has done stole them!"

"Didn't you ever spend any of the money?" asked one neighbor.

"No, no, the coins weren't to spend," said The Miser. "I just loved lookin' at 'em."

"Well, shoot," said another neighbor. "You might as well just look at that there hole for as much good as your money was doin' ya!"

1 The dialect of King Midas could best be described as—

A informal and uses a lot of slang.

B formal and uses more difficult words.

C English with a Greek accent.

D British English.

2 How were King Midas and The Miser alike?

A Both hid their wealth.

B Both loved gold.

C Both had magical powers.

D Both were famous men.

3 Contrast the settings of the stories. Support your answer with details from the text. (3 points)

____

____

____

____

____

____

For **Example 1**, you must think about the **dialect**, or the language used by King Midas. King Midas speaks using formal words such as "glittering destruction." The correct answer is **choice B**.

Example 2 asks you to **compare**, or think about how the main characters of the stories are alike. Read through the answer choices, making sure that the statement is true of BOTH characters. The only statement that is true of both is **choice B**, *Both loved gold.*

Example 3 asks you to **contrast** the settings of the stories. Remember that the setting is the place where a story take place. A good answer should describe the settings of both stories by using examples from both texts.

Good: *The settings of "King Midas" and "The Miser and His Gold" are very different. "King Midas" is set in "the age when gods ruled the earth." The gods have magical powers, and Bacchus grants Midas a wish. The setting of "The Miser and His Gold" is many years ago, but the place is a small village. The people speak using informal words and slang.*

Poor: *The settings of "King Midas" and "The Miser and His Gold" are the same yet different. There are gods in "King Midas." There aren't any gods in "The Miser and His Gold."*

Try It On Your Own

4 Both passages are examples of which genre?

A adventure stories
B mystery stories
C traditional stories or folktales
D realistic fiction

5 Which example from "The Miser and His Gold" BEST shows the dialect used in the story?

A *The following morning, The Miser went to his tree.*
B *He was so busy that he did not see the robber behind the tree . . .*
C *Once upon a time many years ago . . .*
D *"Dagnabbit! My gold coins 're gone!" he cried.*

6 Study the diagram comparing the two passages.

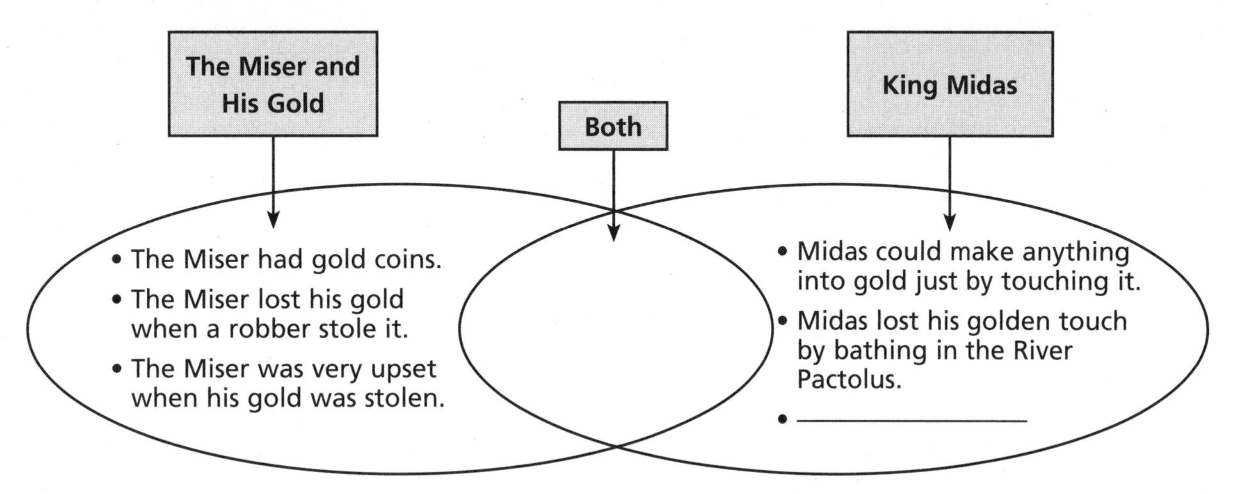

Which of the following facts from "King Midas" is a contrast to the sentence *The Miser was very upset when his gold was stolen*?

A Midas did a good deed for Bacchus.

B Midas received his gold as a reward.

C Midas could not eat anything he touched.

D Midas begged to lose his "golden" touch.

7 Which of the following themes is found in BOTH passages?

A Forgive your enemies.

B Face danger with courage.

C Don't be greedy.

D Keep an open mind.

Test-Taking Tips

1 Remember that a good summary of the main idea should include the main events in the story. Do not include your opinions about the story.

2 To identify the theme of a story, ask yourself, *What is the main idea, message, or lesson of the story?* A story rarely states the theme directly. You must think about how the character responds to challenges in the story. Ask: *What does the character learn? How does he or she grow and change?*

3 To help understand a compare-and-contrast relationship, ask: *How are these things alike? How are they different?*

4 A dialect is the language used by the characters and narrator in the story. Look for words that show that the story takes place in a specific part of the country.

Go for it!

Unit One Practice Test

Estimated time: 20 minutes

Directions: Read the following and then answer the questions that follow.

Night Flashes

Devika lay in bed wide awake and trembling. Her blankets were pulled up over her head. Her eyes were tightly shut so she couldn't see the lightning flashes, and her pillow was around her ears to try to block the sounds of the thunder booming. This time she would try to be brave. She wouldn't give in and go wake up her parents. The last time she did that her brother made fun of her. "Scaredy-cat!" he mocked. "Who's afraid of the little thunderstorm? Devika is!"

But whenever there was a rainstorm, Devika's mind always went back to the night the tornado had struck near their town. Devika had been four years old. In the middle of the night, her parents had grabbed her out of bed and rushed her down to the basement as the tornado sirens screamed around them. They spent a long hour huddled in a basement closet waiting for the storm to pass. In the end the tornado had missed their house, but the memory of that night always came back every time there was a storm.

Devika tried to distract herself by thinking about something else. Then she remembered her science lesson that day. Mr. Parks had explained that you can tell how far away a thunderstorm is by counting the interval between the moment you see the lightning and when you hear the thunder crash.

Devika thought she would give it a try. Counting the seconds kept her mind off her fear. At first there were three seconds and then two seconds. Then the flashes came at the same time as the thunder. "The storm must be right over us," she thought, somewhat curiously. Then the intervals grew longer. There was one second, then two, then three between the lightning and the thunder. "The storm must be going away," she said with a great sigh of relief.

1 Based upon the behavior of Devika's brother, we can infer that he—

A is older than Devika.
B is not afraid of storms.
C has never been in a tornado.
D doesn't like Devika.

2 Why is Devika afraid of storms? Include a direct quotation from the story in your answer. (3 points)

____

____

____

____

____

____

3 The setting of the story is—

A Devika's room.
B a closet in the basement.
C Devika's school.
D Devika's parents' room.

The Big Speech

"Why did I agree to this?" Abigail thought as she wiped her sweaty palms on the new skirt her mother had bought for this special day. She tried to look over her note cards but ended up dropping them all over the floor in a jumbled mess.

"A little nervous, huh?" Hannah, Abigail's friend, asked. Hannah had participated in the speech competition the year before and had won first prize.

"Nervous, no. Terrified, yes." Abigail said, trying to sound funny, but the truth was she was really scared to talk in front of the big crowd.

"I was afraid last year too," Hannah confessed. Abigail was surprised. Hannah had seemed so composed on stage. "Do you want to know my secret?" Hannah asked. "I pretend that everyone in the audience is wearing a silly costume. I imagined Principal Wyatt in a clown costume wearing a bright red nose." That thought was enough to make Abigail smile.

"Good luck out there," Hannah said as she left to join the audience. As she departed, Abigail took a deep breath and pretended that Hannah was wearing a hula costume. With a smile on her face, she went out on the stage.

4 Write a short summary of the "The Big Speech." (3 points)

____

____

____

____

____

____

Directions: Use both "Night Flashes" and "The Big Speech" to answer the following questions.

5 Which of the following is true of the main characters of BOTH stories?

A They speak using formal English.
B They get help from friends.
C They are afraid because of something that happened in the past.
D They figure out how to conquer their fears on their own.

6 What common theme do these passages have?

A Good friends can help you.
B Family will always be there for you.
C You don't have to be a hero.
D You can overcome your fears.

Points Earned/Total = ______/10

Word Choice

Review the Standards (RL.5.4, L.5.5, L.5.5.a, L.5.5.b, RL.5.6)

- Determine the meaning of **figurative language** including **similes**, **metaphors**, and **idioms** in context
- Demonstrate understanding of **nuances** in word meanings
- Describe how **point of view** influences how events are described

Q: What are **similes**, **metaphors**, and **idioms**?

A: Sometimes writers use words or phrases that mean something different from the literal, or actual, meaning of the words. To understand the word or phrase that contains **figurative language**, you have to ask yourself, *What does the writer mean? What is the writer trying to communicate?*

Figurative Language	Description	Example	Explanation
Simile	a comparison of two things using *like* or *as*	The girl is as quiet as a mouse.	The girl is shy; she doesn't talk very much.
Metaphor	a comparison of two things that says one thing *is* another	The quiet girl is a mouse.	The girl is shy; she doesn't talk very much.
Personification	gives human characteristics to nonhuman things	The tree stretched its limbs to the sky.	The tree braches looked like a person stretching their arms up to the sky.
Idiom	an expression that means something very different from the meanings of the individual words	When my dad saw the crack in the television screen, he blew his top.	Dad got really mad and lost his temper.
Adage/Proverb	a saying that contains truth or wisdom about life	The grass is always greener on the other side.	What other people have always looks better than what you have.

Q: What are **nuances** in word meanings?

A: A **nuance** is a slight difference. Some words mean almost the same thing, but have a slightly different feeling associated with them. Consider the difference between the words *cheap* and *inexpensive.* Both words mean "not costing much money." However, the word *cheap* implies that the item is not well made. Understanding nuances in word meaning will help you understand the writer's point of view.

Q: What is **point of view**?

A: **Point of view** has to do with who is telling the story. If a character in the story is describing the events, the story is written in first person. If an outside narrator is telling the story, the story is written in third person. Study the following examples:

First Person: So there I was, last Tuesday at 10:45. Mr. Cole had just given us a surprise quiz to finish in the last 15 minutes of class. (Uses the pronouns *I* and *us.*)

Third person: Now Brer Bear was lucky to find himself with a big old farm with soil richer and darker than he'd ever seen.

Remember that first-person point of view will give you a more direct description of the story, but you will only get one character's side of the story. Third-person point of view often describes the thoughts of several characters. As you read, think about how the point of view influences how the events of the story are described.

Try It

Directions: Read the passage. Then answer the questions that follow.

Run, Carl, Run!

1 The sound of my high-pitched shriek rang out through the neighborhood like a siren screaming a warning alarm. Through the twilight, I ran hard. I moved my feet faster than I ever had in my life. I could hear the panting of *something behind me.*

2 The creature—whatever it was—was huge. As big as an elephant. Maybe bigger. It was brown and had the longest red tongue in the animal kingdom. Its teeth were like a crocodile's pointy chompers. Panting, I felt a stitch in my side. It hurt, causing me to slow down. Would the creature catch me? Would it eat me?

3 Finally, my house loomed before me. With sweat running into my eyes, I could barely see my own front door. I fumbled with the key. I dropped the key. The creature was turning down my front walk!

4 With a superhuman effort, I grabbed the key off the doormat, stuck it in the lock, and threw myself through the open door. Falling on the floor inside, I kicked the door shut behind me.

5 Outside on the porch, I heard the sound of claws skidding up to the door. A few moments passed, and the creature heaved itself against the door and whined. It must really be hungry.

6 Then, and I say this with true terror, I heard a sound scarier than that panting and those claws and that whine. I heard a key in the lock! The creature knew how to come in my house and get me!

7 With a click, the door swung open. "Hey, Carl!"

8 *What?* I thought. *It knows my name?*

9 Then my dad popped through the open door. He turned to pull something big and heavy in after him.

10 "Look, Carl," Dad said. "I adopted this dog at the pound today. He's huge, but he's really just a big teddy bear. Oh, don't worry his bark is much worse than his bite. I was taking him for a walk. We were going to meet you at school and walk you home. But he got loose, and he ran ahead of me. Guess what? He already knows his way home, because he was on the front porch when I caught up to him just now. He's great, isn't he?"

1 When Carl says "I felt a stitch in my side," he means that—

A a pin has gotten stuck in his clothing.
B he is sewing his side with a needle and thread.
C something is tickling him.
D he feels a pain in his side.

2 Which sentence from the passage contains figurative language?

A *Its teeth were like a crocodile's pointy chompers.*
B *With a click, the door swung open.*
C *He turned to pull something big and heavy in after him.*
D *He's great, isn't he?*

3 Which of the following words has nearly the same meaning as the word kicked used in paragraph 4?

A closed
B shut
C slammed
D tapped

Example 1 asks you to identity the meaning of an **idiom**. An idiom is a type of **figurative language** in which the meanings of the individual words do not equal the meaning of the phrase. Carl is not literally sewing a stitch in his side. From the context, we know that Carl feels a pain in his side. The correct answer is **choice D**.

For **Example 2**, you must decide which answer choice contains figurative language. Remember that figurative language is not meant to be understood literally. Figurative language often compares two things. In choice A, the creature's teeth are compared to a crocodile's teeth. This is a **simile**. The correct answer is **choice A**.

Example 3 asks you to think about **nuances** of word meaning. Think about the word *kicked*. You can visualize Carl, scared and desperate, kicking the door shut with his foot. The words *closed* and *shut* imply that the action is done in a calm manner. The verb *tapped* implies that the door was shut with very little effort. The best answer is **choice C**, *slammed*.

Try It On Your Own

4 Reread these sentences from the passage.

The sound of my high-pitched shriek rang out through the neighborhood like a siren screaming a warning alarm.

The underlined phrase is an example of—

A a simile.
B a metaphor.
C personification.
D an idiom.

5 When Carl's dad says the dog is really just a big teddy bear, he means that the dog is—

A a toy.
B harmless.
C actually a bear.
D dangerous.

6 Which of the following words has nearly the same meaning as the word heaved in paragraph 5?

A propped
B threw
C moved
D set

7 Explain the idiom his bark is much worse than his bite. Support your answer with evidence from the text. (3 points)

____

____

____

____

____

Poetry

Review the Standards (RL.5.2, RL.5.5)

- Determine the theme of a poem
- Explain how a speaker in a poem feels
- Explain how stanzas fit together in a poem

Q: How do I understand and interpret poetry?

A: Poetry is different from prose. Poetry's main focus is to communicate emotions by using the best and most precise words. That's why poetry is usually shorter. Poems often contain sound devices such as alliteration or rhyme. Sometimes poetry has rhythm. All of these things work together to communicate the theme, or the main idea, of the poem.

The following chart will help you understand some elements you will often find in poetry.

Term	Explanation	Example
Rhyme	pattern of words that sound the same	And now the pitcher holds the ball, and now he lets it go, And now the air is shattered by the force of Casey's blow.
Alliteration	words with the same beginning consonant sound	The bees buzzed around the buds.
Onomatopoeia	words that sound like what they mean	The lightning crashed and boomed.
Stanza	lines of a poem grouped together	Oh, somewhere in this favored land the sun is shining bright, The band is playing somewhere, and somewhere hearts are light, And somewhere men are laughing, and little children shout; But there is no joy in Mudville—mighty Casey has struck out. (This stanza is made up of four lines.)
Meter	Pattern of stressed and unstressed syllables	TYger, TYger, BURNing BRIGHT IN the FORests OF the NIGHT

 Try It

Directions: Read the poem. Then answer the questions that follow.

Shadow March

by Robert Louis Stevenson

All around the house is the jet-black night;
It stares through the window-pane;
It crawls in the corners, hiding from the light,
And it moves with the moving flame.

Now my heart goes a-beating like a drum,
With the breath of Bogie in my hair,
And all around the candle the crooked shadows come,
And go marching along up the stair.

The shadow of the balusters, the shadow of the lamp,
The shadow of the child that goes to bed—
All the wicked shadows coming, tramp, tramp, tramp,
With the black night overhead.

1 Which line communicates how the speaker is feeling?

A *All around the house is the jet-black night;*
B *And it moves with the moving flame.*
C *Now my heart goes a-beating like a drum,*
D *The shadow of the child that goes to bed—*

2 Read the following line.

All the wicked shadows coming, tramp, tramp, tramp,

The word *tramp* is repeated—

A to help the reader hear the sound of the marching shadows.
B because the poet couldn't think of another word.
C because a tramp had broken into the house.
D to help the reader see how dark the night was.

3 Which stanza describes the night? How is the night described? Support your answer with examples from the text. (3 points)

____

____

____

____

____

____

____

____

Example 1 asks you to find the line that helps you understand how the speaker is feeling. If you read through the answer choices, you will notice that only one line uses the pronoun *my* and describes the speaker's emotions. The other lines describe what the speaker sees. The best answer is **choice C**.

Example 2 asks you to think about the repetition of the word *tramp* in the line *All the wicked shadows coming, tramp, tramp, tramp.* You can eliminate choices B and C right away since you know that poets always choose their words carefully, and the word *tramp* is not referring to a person. The repetition of the word helps you hear the sound of footsteps. The correct answer is **choice A**.

Example 3 asks you to think about the ideas communicated in a stanza. First, you must identify which stanza describes the night. Then, you must explain how the night is described. A good answer will refer to specific lines in the poem.

Good: *The first stanza in the poem describes the night. It is "jet-black." Like a person, it "stares through" the windows, "crawls in the corners," and avoids the light.*

A poor answer will not identify the correct stanza and will not refer to specific evidence from the text.

Poor: *The third stanza describes the night. It is dark and scary.*

Try It On Your Own

4 Which line is the BEST example of alliteration?

A *All around the house is the jet-black night;*

B *And go marching along up the stair.*

C *With the black night overhead.*

D *And all around the candle the crooked shadows come,*

5 Stanza 3 helps the reader understand—

A what is going on outside the house.
B what time of year it is.
C what objects are casting the shadows.
D what the child does before going to bed.

6 Explain the theme, or main idea, of the poem. Support your answer using details from the poem. (3 points)

____

____

____

____

____

____

____

____

Test-Taking Tips

1 Figurative language is not meant to be taken literally. Think about what the author is trying to communicate by comparing two different things.

2 Poetry often uses sound to communicate the meaning of the poem. Think about how the rhyme, rhythm, and stanzas work together to create the main idea, or the theme, of the poem.

3 To find the point of view of the passage, ask, *Who is telling the story?* If one of the characters is telling the story, then the passage is in first person. If a narrator is telling the story, the passage is in third person.

Go for it!

Unit Two Practice Test

Estimated time: 50 minutes

Directions: Read the following poem, and then answer the questions that follow.

Stopping

Coasting down the sidewalk
On my skateboard,
Free as a bird,
Then I pass the new kid's house
And keep on coasting.

Pedaling down the sidewalk
On my bike,
Wild as the west wind,
Then I pass the new kid's house
And keep on pedaling.

Dribbling down the sidewalk
With my basketball,
I am a blazing star,
Then I pass the new kid's house
And stop dribbling.

I am back in time
On my porch,
And *my* house is the new kid's house,
I am a crushed tin can in an empty lot
Because no one's stopping.

Dribbling up the walk
Of the new kid's house,
I am the first ripple in the pond.
Then I ring the doorbell
And start smiling.

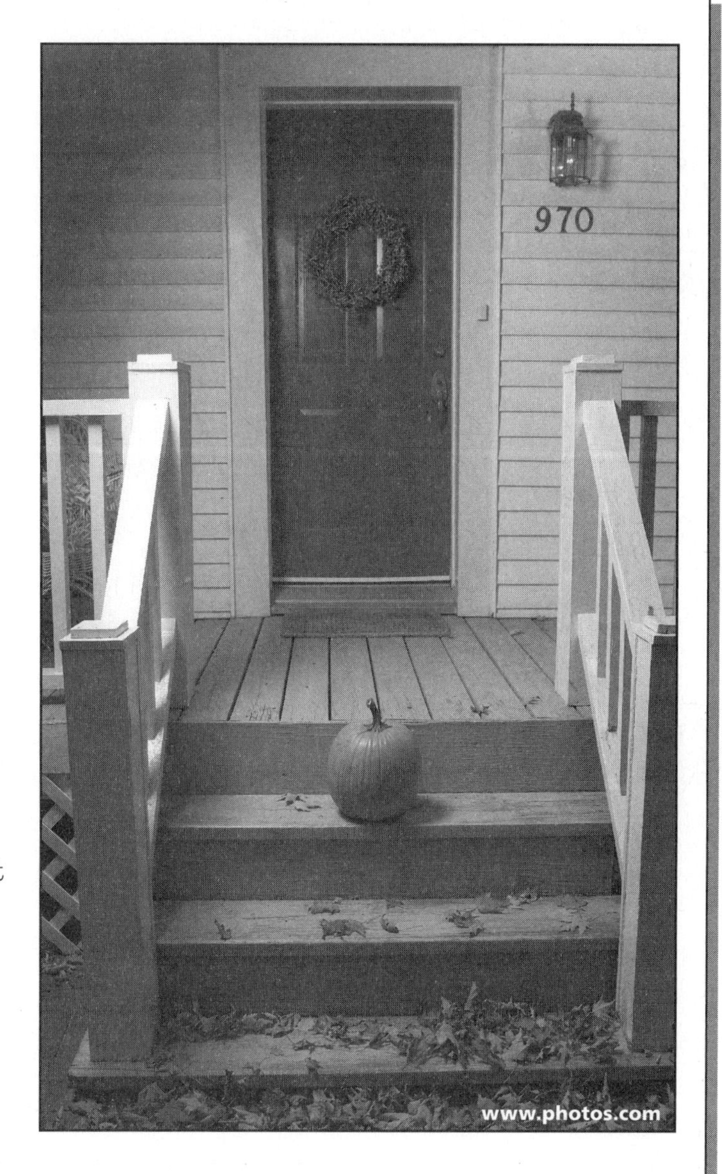

1 The poem is written from the point of view of—

A the new kid in the neighborhood.

B a basketball player.

C a dog in the neighborhood.

D a kid who remembers being new in the neighborhood.

2 Read the following line from the poem.

I am a crushed tin can in an empty lot

This figure of speech communicates the speaker's feelings of—

A loneliness.
B anger.
C joy.
D fear.

3 The phrase "I am the first ripple in the pond" is—

A a metaphor.
B a simile.
C an idiom.
D a proverb.

4 In stanza 3, the word *dribbling* means the speaker is—

A bouncing a basketball and walking down the sidewalk.
B crawling along the sidewalk.
C spitting on the sidewalk.
D kicking the ball down the sidewalk.

5 What is the theme of the poem?

A Treat others the way you want to be treated.
B It is good to take risks.
C Exercise is good for your body.
D Don't be a bully.

6 Explain how stanza 4 is different from the other stanzas. How do the differences in stanza 4 help communicate the meaning of the poem? Support your answer using details from the poem. (3 points)

____

____

____

____

____

____

Points Earned/Total = _____/8

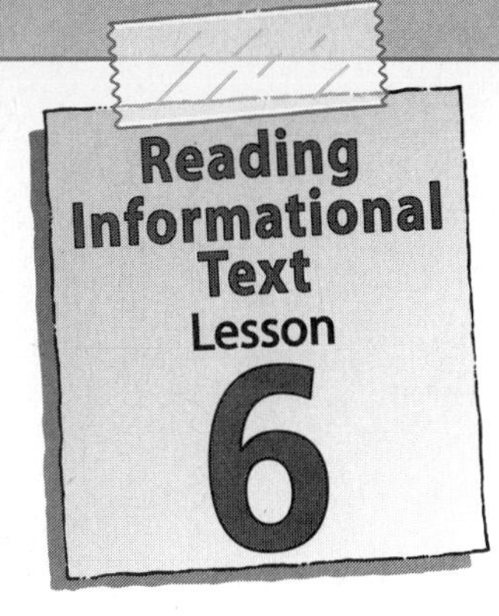

Quote, Infer, and Summarize

Review the Standards (RI.5.1, RI.5.2)

- **Quote** a text accurately
- Make an **inference**
- **Summarize** the text

Q: How do I **quote** the text?

A: When you use the author's exact words, you are quoting the text. Be sure to copy the author's words and punctuation exactly, without adding or removing anything. Place quotation marks (" ") around the quotation.

Q: How do I make an **inference**?

A: An **inference** is a reasonable guess based on details in the text and your own knowledge. For instance, you may read an article about a boy who has not brushed his teeth regularly for months. He has eaten lots of candy. Now he feels a pain in his tooth. You know that cavities are caused by not taking care of your teeth. You can make the following inference:

Inference	Supporting Evidence
The boy has a cavity in his tooth.	• He has not brushed his teeth regularly. • He has eaten a lot of sugar. • He has a pain in his tooth.

Q: What should I include in a **summary**?

A: A **summary** is a shortened version of the main ideas in a selection. Only the most important ideas are included in a summary. Do not include small details or your own ideas or opinions.

Try It

Directions: Read the passage. Then answer the questions that follow.

1 Nowadays, most American children receive a variety of vaccinations. These shots, usually injections of a small dose of a disease, make the children immune to that disease in the future. Vaccinations spare people from many life-threatening ailments.

2 The first vaccine, for smallpox, was developed in 1796 by Edward Jenner. Jenner showed that by infecting a patient with cowpox, a weaker, less dangerous disease, he could prevent patients from getting the more serious smallpox. Scientists knew of Jenner's work, but it took 75 years for them to take the next step. At that time, Louis Pasteur learned to weaken the actual disease that people caught. His work resulted in a successful vaccine for rabies.

3 A number of other vaccines were created in the early 1900s. Often, several scientists worked on vaccinations for the same disease, each contributing helpful ideas. German doctor Emil von Behring is usually given credit for a successful diphtheria vaccine, which he announced in 1913. Twenty-four years later, South African doctor Max Theiler put forth a successful vaccine for yellow fever.

4 It took many years to come up with a good vaccine for polio, a crippling disease that often affected children. In 1954, Dr. Jonas Salk tested an injection that was generally successful, but it did cause a few actual cases of the disease. This opened the door for a different polio vaccine, one that was taken in liquid form. This vaccine was introduced six years later by Dr. Albert Sabin. Both Salk's and Sabin's vaccines have been improved and are still in use.

1 Which of the following ideas should be included in a summary of this selection?

A American children receive a variety of vaccinations.
B The first vaccine was developed in 1796.
C Cowpox was less dangerous than smallpox.
D Many scientists knew about Edward Jenner's work.

2 Based on details in the passage, you can infer that—

A some scientists give up on their work because it is hard.
B each scientist kept his or her work a secret from other scientists.
C vaccinations are worth the long hard work of creating them.
D most vaccinations are tested on cows.

3 Why did it take many years to develop a good vaccine for polio? Use one quotation from the passage in your answer. (3 points)

____

____

____

____

____

Example 1 is a question about **summarizing** the selection. Remember that a summary should contain only the major ideas in a passage. Read through the answer choices and decide if each choice is a major idea or a minor detail. Only choice B gives an important detail that should be contained in a summary. The best answer is **choice B.**

You must make an **inference** to answer **Example 2**. Look for details in the passage that support the inference. The passage does not mention scientists giving up on their work or keeping their work secret, so choices A and B are incorrect. The passage does not mention testing vaccines on cows, so you can rule out choice D too. The passage does give details about the many years of work necessary to develop a vaccine. **Choice C** is correct.

To answer **Example 3**, you must think about details in paragraph 4. A good response includes a **quotation** from paragraph 4 to support your answer.

Good: *It took scientists years to make a good polio vaccine because at first there was a problem. The first vaccine caused some people to get polio. "This opened the door for a different polio vaccine, one that was taken in liquid form." It took six years for the next polio vaccine to be made. Even after that, scientists still worked to make both vaccines better.*

This is a poor response because it doesn't use a quotation from the passage.

Poor: *It took a lot of years to make the polio vaccine. Some things worked and some things didn't.*

Try It On Your Own

4 Which of the following ideas should NOT be included in a summary of this selection?

A Many vaccines were developed in the 1900s.

B Vaccinations can spare people from many diseases.

C One doctor who developed a vaccine was South African.

D Pasteur learned to make a weaker form of a disease that people caught.

5 Which of the following best summarizes the information in paragraph 3?

A Many scientists worked on vaccinations for the same disease.

B The diphtheria vaccine was announced in 1913.

C A vaccine for yellow fever was discovered in 1937.

D Vaccines for diphtheria and yellow fever were developed in the 1900s.

6 How important is teamwork in the development of vaccines? Use one quotation from the passage to support your answer. (3 points)

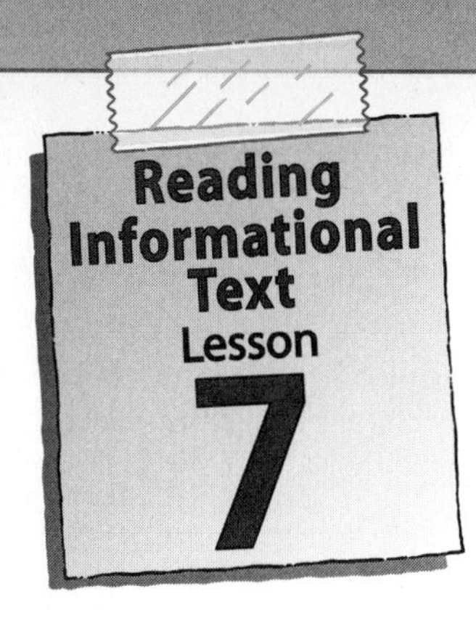

Main Ideas and Supporting Details

Review the Standards (RI.5.2, RI.5.3)

- Explain how **main ideas** are supported by **key details**
- Explain the relationships between ideas in a text

Q: What are **main ideas**?

A: **Main ideas** are the chief points that an author makes. Each paragraph has a main idea. The main idea of each paragraph works together to support the main idea of the entire passage.

Q: How do **key details** support main ideas?

A: **Details** support the main idea by giving facts, examples, or reasons. Ask yourself, *How does the writer support the main idea of the paragraph/passage?* The details a writer uses to support his main idea will depend upon his purpose for writing. Study the following chart.

Purpose of Passage	Main Idea	Examples of Supporting Details
Explain the life of Martin Luther King Jr.	Martin Luther King Jr. was a leader in the fight for equal rights of African Americans.	He was born on January 15, 1929. In 1960, he was arrested while protesting segregation at a lunch counter in Atlanta, Georgia.
Explain the steps for making tortillas	Making tortillas is not difficult when you follow these simple steps.	First, combine 2 cups *masa harina* and 1½ to 2 cups of very warm water. Next, shape the dough into a small ball.
Persuade people to eat more fruits and vegetables	Eating more fruits and vegetables will help you be healthier.	Fruits and vegetables are low in calories. Vegetables have high amounts of vitamins to prevent illness.

Q: How do ideas in a text relate to one another?

A: As you read, look for how the ideas in the text are related. Watch for cause and effect relationships and similarities and differences. Study the following chart.

To find these relationships, look for the following words in the passage.			
Causes/Reasons	**Effects/Results**	**Similarities**	**Differences**
because because of caused due to since	as a result resulted in so for this reason	in the same way likewise similarly and	unlike however on the other hand in contrast

Try It

Directions: Read the passage. Then answer the questions that follow.

A Clownlike Animal

The Old World chameleon is a lizard found mainly in Africa. Although this creature looks like a small dragon, it behaves more like a clown. The chameleon has eyeballs that can rotate. Upon spotting an insect, both of the chameleon's eyes focus on the bug. This gives the lizard a foolish, cross-eyed look.

The chameleon's tongue is extremely long and odd-looking. Chameleons use their tongues to pluck insects from the air, then reel them back into their mouths like eager fishermen pulling in their lines.

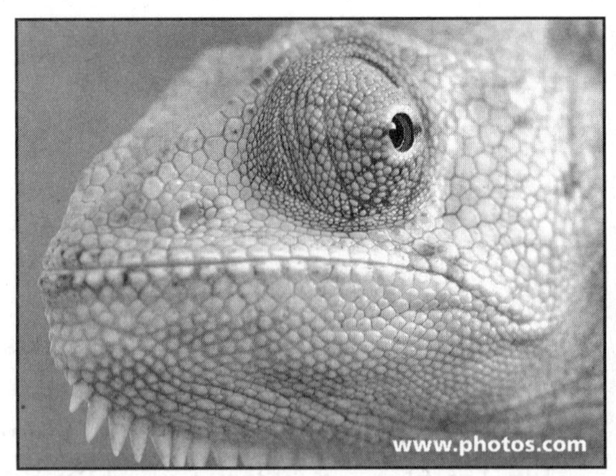
www.photos.com

Chameleons spend most of their time in trees, sometimes jumping down when frightened. Instead of landing gracefully, they fall like a sack of potatoes. When they move on land, the lizards walk on the tips of their claws with a clumsy, wobbling gait.

1 Why did the author compare the Old World chameleon to a clown? Use details from the passage to support your answer. (3 points)

____

____

____

____

____

2 A chameleon is able to rotate its—

A tongue.
B eyeballs.
C claws.
D tail.

3 According to the passage, what causes the Old World chameleon to jump down from a tree?

A hunger
B fright
C thirst
D anger

To answer **Example 1**, you must think about the relationship between two ideas in the text: the Old World chameleon and clowns. A good response includes at least two details from the text to support your answer.

Good: *The writer compares the chameleon to a clown because it can seem goofy. For example, the chameleon's eyeballs can rotate in a funny way. When it looks at an insect, it goes cross-eyed. This is something a clown might do. Another thing that is like a clown is the way they just thump down like a sack of potatoes. They also walk funny because they walk on their tiptoes.*

Below is a poor response. It doesn't use specific details from the passage to answer the question.

Poor: *The chameleon is funny, and clowns are funny. They both can make you laugh. They both are goofy. The chameleon is really a lizard, not a clown.*

Example 2 asks you about a **supporting detail** mentioned in the passage. Supporting details provide information or relate specific facts about the main idea. The third sentence says, "The chameleon has eyeballs that can rotate." The correct answer is **choice B**, *eyeballs.*

To answer **Example 3**, you must identify a cause and effect relationship. In this example, the effect is chameleons jumping from trees. What causes them to do this? The passage states, "Chameleons spend most of their time in trees, sometimes jumping down when frightened." The cause for their jumping is *fright.* **Choice B** is correct.

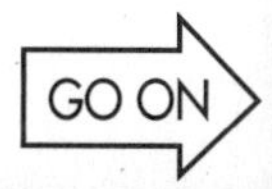

Try It On Your Own

Directions: Read the following passage and answer the questions that follow.

The History of Labor Day

Have you ever wondered how Labor Day started? It all began with a strike in a community called Pullman, Illinois. The town had been built by George Pullman in 1880 to house the workers at his company that built railroad cars. Pullman, on the southern border of Chicago, was a fairly nice place to live.

In 1893, things changed in Pullman. George Pullman's business was not doing well because he did not have enough orders for railroad cars. Pullman had to dismiss hundreds of workers, and the workers who remained had to take salary cuts of 25 percent or more. Pullman did not lower rents on the houses, though, and he would not let his workers move somewhere else. People worked for less money, but they had to pay the same rent. The workers knew this was not fair, so they walked out on their jobs. They went on strike.

People all over the country heard about the strike. Many people were angry about the way the workers were treated. The workers at Pullman had recently become part of a union, and railroad workers across the country joined the Pullman strike. It was the first nationwide strike in America. President Grover Cleveland sent in troops to break up the strike, and there was violence.

Workers in Pullman and in many other parts of the country had been asking for several years for a special day to honor workers. In 1893, many of them were particularly angry with Grover Cleveland because of the action he had taken against the strikers. President Cleveland was up for re-election, and the strikes were making him look bad. To show that he cared about the workers' situation and to receive the workers' votes, Cleveland signed a bill to make Labor Day a national holiday to honor American workers. People in New York City held parades that were similar to the protest marches held by union workers.

Labor Day in the United States is celebrated on the first Monday in September. Many people do not have to go to work on Labor Day, and students do not have to be in school. People march in parades and enjoy picnics with families and friends. Nowadays, though, many people celebrate Labor Day for a different reason. They regard Labor Day as the last weekend of the summer.

4 Explain how some of George Pullman's actions were unfair? Use details from the passage to support your answer. (3 points)

"Pullman did not lower the rents on the houses, though, and he would not let his workers move somewhere else. People worked for less money, but they had to pay the same rent" This was not fair for the workers.

5 Why did George Pullman cut his workers' salaries in 1893?

A He was unhappy with their work.

B He wanted to keep them from striking.

C His railroad car business was not doing well.

D He wanted them to organize the first Labor Day.

6 Which of the following is the BEST summary of the passage?

A Labor Day exists because of the Pullman railroad workers' strike. The strike, over high rents and no jobs, was broken up violently by soldiers sent by President Grover Cleveland. To regain workers' support, Cleveland agreed to a holiday to honor them, a holiday still celebrated today.

B The Pullman railroad workers lived in a small town on the southern edge of Chicago. Their houses had been built by George Pullman. They had a strike, and people all over the country heard about it.

C People still celebrate Labor Day today. They have picnics and parades, and they don't go to work. Labor Day is the first Monday in September. We have Labor Day because in 1893 some workers had a strike.

D The Pullman strike was the first nationwide strike. The Pullman workers were railroad workers. They lived in a town that George Pullman had built for them. President Grover Cleveland sent in troops to break up the strike.

7 Which detail supports the idea that President Cleveland wanted to show that he cared about workers?

A *. . . Cleveland signed a bill to make Labor Day a national holiday to honor American workers.*

B *President Cleveland was up for re-election . . .*

C *. . . the strikes were making him look bad.*

D *Labor Day in the United States is celebrated on the first Monday in September.*

Test-Taking Tips

1 To make an inference, find clues and information in the text. Then combine the clues with what you already know. You should always be able to support an inference with evidence from the text.

2 To write a summary, first read the text and mark the main idea and most important details. Use this information to guide your writing.

3 To identify the main idea of a paragraph, look for the topic sentence. You can also ask yourself, *What is this paragraph mostly about?*

4 When answering questions about supporting details, more than one answer choice may seem correct. Choose the answer that gives specific information about the main idea.

Go for it!

Unit Three Practice Test

Estimated time: 20 minutes

Directions: Read the following passage, and then answer the questions that follow.

Having the Right to Vote

Less than a century ago, women had few rights in this country. They could not own property or keep any money they earned if they were married. And they could not vote. Many women saw the right to vote, called *suffrage*, as an important goal, and they struggled for many years to achieve it. This struggle is known as the suffrage movement.

Beginnings

Most people point to the year 1848 as the start of the suffrage movement. At that time two determined women, Elizabeth Cady Stanton and Lucretia Mott, called together a meeting in Seneca Falls, New York. The people at the meeting made a list of women's rights they thought were most important. The right to vote was among them. Not long afterward, Susan B. Anthony joined the movement. Anthony was a strong speaker who could deliver the messages that Stanton wrote. A women named Lucy Stone also joined the movement and gave powerful speeches.

Struggles

In 1870, the Fifteenth Amendment to the Constitution was ratified. It gave all citizens, including former slaves, the right to vote. However, it did not mention females. Stanton and Anthony thought that women should be included in the amendment; Lucy Stone, however, thought that women should fight a separate battle. Her position was that the injustice to slaves was so great that it should be dealt with first. And so a deep division developed in the suffragette movement.

Anthony and Stanton's group decided to take bold action. In 1872, Anthony and other women voted in a presidential election. They were arrested for voting illegally, and the trial drew much attention to the suffrage movement. In 1878, the group tried to convince U.S. senators to introduce an amendment to the Constitution making it legal for women to vote. The amendment was introduced every year for over forty years without success. Meanwhile, Lucy Stone and her group worked for women's voting rights in individual states.

Success

In 1890, the two groups joined again to form the National American Woman Suffrage Association. Women gradually gained more opportunities. Several states allowed women to vote in local elections, but national voting was still closed to them.

Women became more outspoken in demanding voting rights, and new, younger leaders took over the cause. Protests were held in many cities and even in front of the White House. Some of the women were thrown in jail. But in 1918, President Wilson agreed to support the women's suffrage amendment that was still in the Congress, and it passed. In early 1920, Tennessee, the final state needed to ratify the amendment, voted in support of it. And so the Nineteenth Amendment became law.

1 The main ideas in this passage are organized by—

A cause and effect
B chronological order
C problem and solution
D comparison and contrast

2 The passage is organized this way to—

A show the sequence of events in the women's suffrage movement.
B compare the Fifteenth Amendment to the Nineteenth Amendment.
C explain the reasons for the disagreement between Stone, Anthony, and Stanton.
D compare the women's suffrage movement to other movements.

3 What is the main idea of the second paragraph?

A *Most people point to the year 1848 as the start of the suffrage movement.*
B *At that time two determined women, Elizabeth Cady Stanton and Lucretia Mott, called together a meeting in Seneca Falls, New York.*
C *Not long afterward, Susan B. Anthony joined the movement.*
D *A women named Lucy Stone also joined the movement and gave powerful speeches.*

4 Read the statement below.

The people at the first meeting in 1848 began their document with the words "all men and women are created equal."

In which section of the passage would this supporting detail fit best?

A introductory paragraph
B under the heading "Beginnings"
C under the heading "Struggles"
D under the heading "Success"

5 Based upon the passage, we can infer that Elizabeth Cady Stanton—

A was a good writer but was not a strong speaker.
B didn't want help with her work.
C was not in favor of women voting in local elections.
D approved of slavery.

6 Which of the following details should NOT be included in a summary of the passage?

A The right to vote was called "suffrage."
B Elizabeth Stanton and Susan B. Anthony worked together for women's suffrage.
C The Fifteenth Amendment gave former slaves the right to vote.
D In 1920, the Nineteenth Amendment was ratified, giving women the right to vote.

7 Which quotation from the passage explains the cause of a deep division in the suffragette movement?

A *A women named Lucy Stone also joined the movement and gave powerful speeches.*
B *Lucy Stone, however, thought that women should fight a separate battle.*
C *Meanwhile, Lucy Stone and her group worked for women's voting rights in individual states.*
D *They were arrested for voting illegally, and the trial drew much attention to the suffrage movement.*

8 Write a short summary of the section "Success." Include one direct quote in your summary. (3 points)

____

____

____

____

____

____

____

____

____

____

____

Points Earned/Total = _____/10

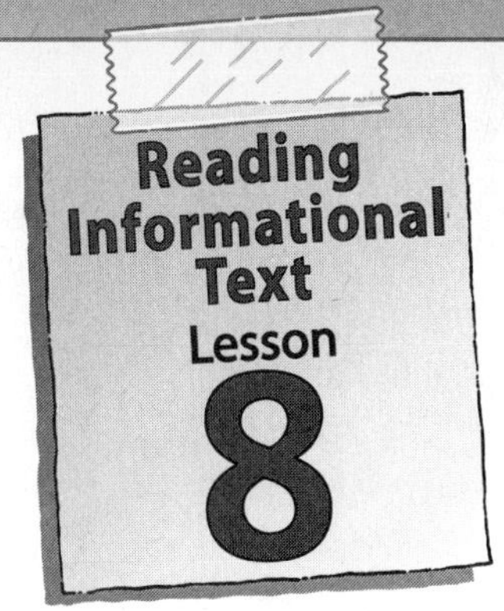

Using Multiple Texts

Review the Standards (RI.5.5, RI.5.6, RI.5.7, RI.5.9)

- Locate an answer to a question from multiple texts
- **Integrate** information from several texts
- Compare and contrast the **structure** of two texts
- Analyze the **point of view** of multiple accounts of a topic or event

Q: How do I use multiple texts to answer a question?

A: To answer a question using multiple texts, you must **integrate,** or bring together, information from all the texts. Look for details, facts, or examples that relate to the same idea. Then ask yourself questions: *What do I learn from each text? Is the information the same or different?*

Q: How are texts **structured**?

A: The events, ideas, and information in texts may be arranged by chronology (time order), cause and effect, problem and solution, or comparison and contrast.

Q: How do I analyze **point of view**?

A: When reading informational text, **point of view** has to do with a person's opinion about the events or topics they are describing. For example, if you read a soldier's account of a battle from the Revolutionary War and an account by General George Washington, their points of view about the difficulty and progress of the battle may be very different. If you read two articles about how to stop global warming, one writer might suggest requiring people to use public transportation instead of driving cars. A different writer might suggest switching to solar and wind power instead of burning coal and other fossil fuels. To analyze point of view, think about how the writers agree or disagree.

Try It

Directions: Read the passages. Then answer the questions that follow.

The Steamer Brothers

1 The Stanley twins, Francis and Freelan, were born on June 1, 1849, in Kingfield, Maine, and loved tinkering with things even as boys. As young men, the twins opened a factory that produced photographic plates. In the fall of 1896, Francis and Freelan attended a local fair where they saw a demonstration of a

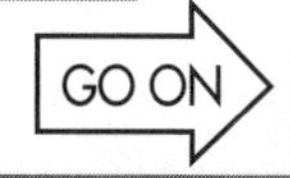

French steam-driven car. The brothers were inspired. After the fair, the brothers began to develop a steam car of their own.

2 The brothers formed a car company in 1898 and produced their first steam car, which was called The Flying Teapot. An instant success, the car was easy to run and achieved a top speed of 35 miles per hour (56 kph), quite fast for the turn of the century. One negative was that the driver had to stop every ten miles or so to refill the engine with water. In 1902, the brothers formed the Stanley Motor Carriage Company. They held various events to promote their steam cars, including racing up mountains and racing against gas-powered cars. Eventually, the Stanleys sold their photographic plate business and concentrated on the manufacture of their steam cars, or Stanley Steamers.

3 In 1906, one of their cars—The Rocket, driven by Stanley employee Fred Marriott—set the world's record for the fastest mile: 28.2 seconds, which is a speed of more than 127 miles per hour (204 kph). In 1918, tragedy struck. Francis was killed when he swerved to avoid an object in the middle of a mountain road and plunged down an embankment near Ipswich, Massachusetts. At the time of his death, the Stanley Motor Company had suspended automobile production to build machines used in World War I. After the war, Henry Ford's Model T soon came to dominate the American automobile industry. Developments in gas-powered engines, and the limitations of steam cars, signalled the end of the steam-auto era. The Stanley Motor Carriage Company ceased production in 1924. Freelan Oscar Stanley died in 1940 in Boston.

Running on Steam

1 If history had worked out a little differently, people might be driving steam-powered cars today. In 1897, Francis E. and Freelan O. Stanley built the first practical steam-engine car. Called the Stanley Steamer, it was a perfect automobile in many ways. Unlike modern gas-powered cars, it was quiet and caused little pollution. Its engine was so simple that it had only fifteen moving parts. There was no transmission in a Stanley, and there was no need for a clutch to shift gears. In addition, the Stanley Steamer was as fast as, if not faster than, most modern cars.

2 The Stanleys' idea of a steam-engine car was not a new one. In 1769, a Frenchman named Nicolas Cugnot built a steam-powered vehicle. This huge machine had three wheels and moved at a speed of three miles per hour. Its engine was heavy, however, and getting up steam was a slow process. Many other inventors tried to improve on Cugnot's design. One such car was displayed at a fair that F.E. and F.O. Stanley visited in 1896. After looking at the car, the twin brothers decided they could build a much better one.

3 The Stanley brothers' car was indeed well designed. For one thing, it was easier to start than other cars of that period. The driver of a Stanley Steamer simply lit

a fire in the car's boiler. Then he or she waited for the water to steam. After the driver opened a few valves, the car was ready to go. And go it did—up to 150 miles per hour!

4 So what happened to the steam-powered car? One reason it never became widely popular is that the Stanley brothers didn't work hard at selling their car. They made fewer than 1,000 automobiles a year. They were also slow in changing the design of the car to correct safety problems. Meanwhile, other inventors were busy working on gasoline-powered cars. In 1908, Henry Ford introduced the Model T Ford at a cost of $850. Since the car was cheap, powerful, and dependable, Americans eagerly bought Model Ts. As people stopped buying the more expensive steamers, over 100 steam automobile companies closed. The Stanley brothers' company was one of the few that remained. In 1917, however, it was sold. And eight years later, the company closed down. The short era of the steamer was over.

5 But Stanleys have not disappeared altogether. Along with Maxwells, Model Ts, and other remarkable cars of the era, Stanley Steamers are avidly collected by antique-car lovers. On sunny summer weekends, you may see strings of such fine old vehicles cruising along the highway, going or coming from vintage-car meets and rallies.

1 Information in the passage "The Steamer Brothers" is arranged in chronological order. How does the structure of "Running on Steam" compare? Use details from BOTH selections to support your answer. (3 points)

____

____

____

____

____

2 Both passages explain that the Stanley brothers first saw a steam-powered car—

A when Henry Ford demonstrated one.
B in their photographic plate factory.
C at a local fair.
D in France.

3 In "Running on Steam," the author believes that the Stanleys' cars didn't become widely popular for all the following reasons EXCEPT—

A people now collect steam-powered cars.
B the cars were very expensive.
C Henry Ford's cars were more affordable.
D the Stanleys didn't correct safety problems with the cars.

4 Read the following sentence from "Running on Steam."

One reason it never became widely popular is that the Stanley brothers didn't work hard at selling their car.

Which of the following facts from "The Steamer Brothers" gives a different point of view than the sentence above?

A The Stanley twins loved tinkering with things.
B The Stanley's Rocket set the record for the fastest mile.
C The Stanleys promoted their car by holding races against gas-powered cars.
D Francis Stanley was killed in a car accident.

Example 1 asks you to compare the **structures** of the two passages. A good response identifies the structure of each passage and tells how the structures are alike or different.

Good: *The first passage gives events in chronological order. It describes major events in the Stanley brothers' lives. In contrast, "Running on Steam" skips around in time, from 1897 to 1769 to 1908. It is organized by comparison and contrast. First, the Stanley Steamer is compared to Nicolas Cugnot's steam-engine car. Next, the Stanley Steamer is compared to Henry Ford's gas-powered car.*

The following is a poor response. It doesn't use details from BOTH passages to answer the question.

Poor: *The first passage gives events in chronological order. This means that the writer describes each event in the order that it happened. This is one type of structure.*

Example 2 is a question about **integrating** information from both passages. To answer the question, read the answer choices, and then check with the passages to confirm your answer. You will find that both passages explain that the Stanleys saw a steam-powered car demonstrated at a fair. **Choice C** is correct.

To answer **Example 3**, you must think about the **point of view** of the writer of "Running on Steam." The question asks you to think about the reasons why steam-powered cars did not become widely popular. These reasons were given in paragraph 4. The only one not given is choice A. The fact that people collect steam-powered cars is not a reason why they didn't become popular back then. **Choice A** is correct.

Example 4 asks you about how the **points of view** of the two passages are different. You must think about which answer choice gives a different point of view than the example sentence, which states that the Stanleys didn't work hard at selling their car. Choice C gives the fact that the Stanleys promoted their car by holding races against gas-powered cars. The answer is **choice C.**

Try It On Your Own

Sara Hashmi

Directions: Read the passages. Then answer the questions that follow.

The Start of the American Revolution

In September of 1774, delegates from 12 of the American colonies met to determine how to respond to harsh laws passed by the British. They decided to support Massachusetts, which had been hardest hit by these laws. Agreements were reached to boycott all British goods and to not sell any American products to Britain.

Tensions continued to rise. In Massachusetts, groups of minutemen—citizens ready to fight at a minute's notice—trained for battle. Large groups of British forces began to arrive in Boston.

British commander General Gage learned in early 1775 that the minutemen had stored a large supply of guns in the village of Concord, about 20 miles northwest of Boston. Realizing that the loss of these guns would severely hurt the minutemen's ability to fight, Gage organized a secret march to Concord to capture them. Late on the evening of April 18, his troops set off from Boston. But the minutemen were watching. They quickly put two lanterns in the belfry of Boston's Old North Church, their signal that the British were coming to take the secret stash of weapons.

When the colonists saw the signal, they began to warn the people in the nearby towns. Riders set out calling from house to house, "The British are coming!" One of these riders was Paul Revere, a silversmith who was also a supporter of independence for the colonies.

By the next morning the British had gotten as far as Lexington, but the minutemen were ready for them. Shots were exchanged, and eight minutemen were killed. The American Revolutionary War had begun.

A World War Begins

The beginning of World War I was like a pebble splashing into a pond. A single action caused a ripple of effects felt throughout the world and began The First World War.

The countries of Europe had been fighting for centuries. Big countries became bigger by taking land from smaller countries. Nations made alliances, agreeing to protect one another.

The German Empire was led by Kaiser Wilhelm. This empire was very aggressive and had a strong alliance with Austria-Hungary.

On June 28, 1914, Archduke Ferdinand was shot during an official visit to a neighboring country. The gunman was Gavrilo Princip. He didn't want Austria-Hungary to rule Serbia, his homeland.

On July 28, Austria-Hungary declared war on Serbia. Russia came to Serbia's aid. Germany joined Austria-Hungary to help fight Russia. France and Russia were allies, so France came to Russia's assistance.

Within two months, most of Europe was involved in a war that would last for four years. Germany and its partners were called the Central Powers. The countries opposing them were known as the Allied Powers, or Allies.

5 A similarity between the two passages is that they BOTH—

A try to persuade the reader that war is bad.
B compare war to a pebble dropped in a pond.
C connect the cause of war to harsh laws.
D tell about events in chronological order.

6 In BOTH of these selections, the focus is on—

A the assassination of a leader.
B events leading to a war.
C how minutemen got their name.
D events in the 1770s.

7 Read the information in this Venn diagram.

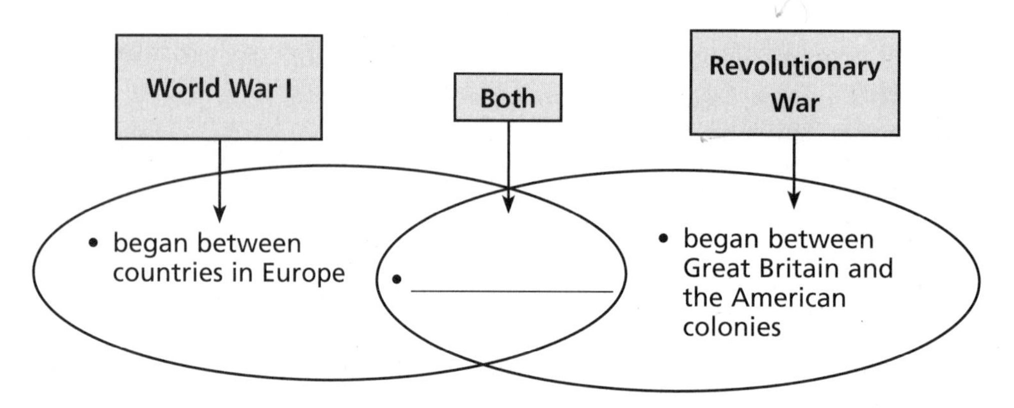

Which information belongs in the blank?

A began with an assassination
B included Paul Revere
C began with a gunshot
D included the Central Powers and the Allied Powers

Directions: Read the following passage. Then answer the questions that follow.

The following is a paraphrase of a letter written in 1774 to General Gage from his British commander, Lord Dartmouth.

"We need to strike now against the rebellious people in Massachusetts. Right now they are a small force, and we should conquer this small force now before they become a larger army and have time to train and gather supplies for war.

It is the opinion of the King that the leaders of the Continental Congress should be arrested and imprisoned. Otherwise they will continue to meet and plan their acts of treason and rebellion. However, any plans to stop the colonists must be kept secret until the moment of action. That way we will succeed, and there will not be any bloodshed. The colonists' army cannot be very strong; they will be no match for your trained men. If the colonists do come against you, don't view this as a reason to start a war."

8 The letter reveals that the British point of view is which of the following?

A The British are afraid because the colonists have a large army.
B The British don't want to take any action against the colonists.
C The British believe the colonists don't have an army or weapons.
D The British believe the colonists are rebelling against the King.

9 Based upon "The Start of the American Revolution," Paul Revere's point of view was that—

A the colonists should give up their weapons to the British.
B war should be avoided at all costs.
C the colonists should obey the King and his laws.
D America should be a separate country from Great Britain.

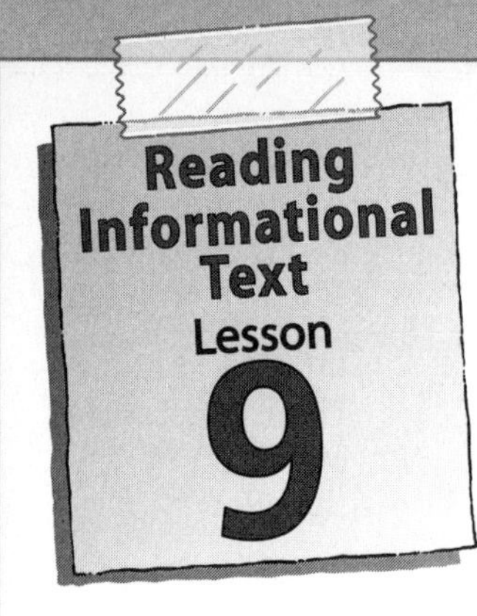

Reasons and Evidence

Review the Standard (RI.5.8)

- Identify and explain **reasons** and supporting **evidence** in a text

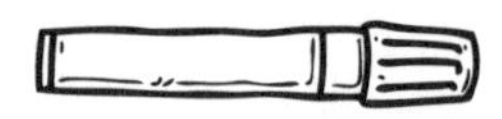

Q: What are **reasons** and **evidence**?

A: When writing about an opinion, writers give **reasons** to support their opinions. Then they support their reasons with **evidence** such as facts, examples, and expert opinions. Study the following example.

Opinion: Smoking in cars should be illegal.

Reason: Secondhand smoke hurts passengers in the car.

Evidence: Secondhand smoke in cars can be ten times more concentrated than the level considered "unhealthy" by the U.S. Environmental Protection Agency.

Try It

Directions: Read the passage. Then answer the questions that follow.

Jerry Spinelli

1 Author Jerry Spinelli didn't always want to write books. When he was a young child growing up in Pennsylvania, his first idea was to become a cowboy. The idea was so exciting that once during his second-grade year he went to school in full cowboy costume (and it wasn't Halloween). The costume included golden-capped toy pistols and boots with spurs. His teacher even encouraged him to entertain his classmates with a cowboy song that day. He sang "I've Got Spurs That Jingle Jangle Jingle."

2 As childhood dreams often do, the dream of a cowboy career faded as Mr. Spinelli grew older. By age ten his passion was baseball, and his new goal was to play shortstop for the New York Yankees. He prepared for this new career by playing Little League baseball throughout junior high and high school. He loved playing baseball. He admits now, however, that he was better at chattering to the pitcher than getting hits.

3 At age sixteen, a big win by his high school football team gave him another idea. He skipped the celebration with friends and instead went home to write a poem about the game. The poem turned out well. In fact, a few days later his hometown newspaper printed it. Becoming a writer suddenly made the most sense of all.

4 Mr. Spinelli went on to study writing at Gettysburg College and The Johns Hopkins University. Then he started writing novels. Every year he sent new manuscripts to publishers, hoping they would accept them. When he wasn't writing novels, Mr. Spinelli worked for a department store magazine to help pay his bills. He worked on the novels whenever he could—during lunch, after work, and on weekends. But publishers continued to reject the novels, one after another.

5 Things began to change after Mr. Spinelli finished his fifth novel. He followed his usual routine of sending copies to many publishers. The problem with this one, the publishers told him, was the main character's age. They didn't think a novel about a thirteen-year-old boy would interest adult readers. Their comments gave Mr. Spinelli an idea. He decided to send the novel to publishers of *children's* books. This decision changed everything. Twenty-five years after writing his first poem, Jerry Spinelli would finally have a published novel. *Space Station Seventh Grade* appeared in bookstores and libraries all over the country. Children loved it.

6 Writing for young readers obviously seemed to suit Mr. Spinelli best. He wrote more novels for and about kids, and publishers gladly accepted them. Memories of his childhood provided plenty of ideas. So did watching his six children grow up. The two children who fought the most were "especially helpful," he says. His longtime interest in sports also helped him find ideas. He wrote about one of his favorite sporting events, the Penn Relays, in the novel *Crash*.

7 Jerry Spinelli has now published twenty-five books for young readers. In 1991 his novel *Maniac Magee* received the Newbery Medal, the highest honor in children's literature.

---

1 All of the following show Mr. Spinelli's great enthusiasm for his dreams EXCEPT—

A he wanted to be a cowboy when he was a child.
B he dressed as a cowboy and sang for his classmates.
C he practiced baseball on teams for many years.
D he worked on novels during lunch and after work.

2 Why did Jerry Spinelli find his two fighting children to be "especially helpful"?

A Their fights were interesting to watch.
B Their fighting drowned out the other noises in his house.
C They were so busy fighting they never bothered him.
D Their disagreements provided him with many ideas for stories.

3 How did things change after Mr. Spinelli completed his fifth novel? Give reasons and evidence from the passage to support your answer. (3 points)

____

____

____

____

____

In **Example 1**, you must decide which details supply **evidence** that Mr. Spinelli showed great enthusiasm for his dreams. You must select the detail that does NOT support this idea. Choices B, C, and D all support this idea. They are all facts about Mr. Spinelli that show he was enthusiastic about his dreams. Choice A, however, only states that he wanted to be a cowboy. It does not describe his enthusiasm. **Choice A** is correct.

To answer **Example 2**, you must identify the **reason** that supports the idea that the fighting children were helpful. First, reread the information in the next to the last paragraph of the article. It tells you that his fighting children were helpful because they "provided plenty of ideas." The only answer choice that gives evidence about providing ideas is choice D. **Choice D** is correct.

Example 3 asks you to give **reasons and evidence** that support the author's statement that things changed after Mr. Spinelli completed his fifth novel. A good response gives at least two details from the passage to explain what changed.

Good: *Some publishers told Mr. Spinelli that the problem with this novel was the main character's age. They didn't think adults would want to read about a thirteen-year-old. This explanation gave Mr. Spinelli an idea. He sent his work to children's publishers. Childern's publishers loved his writing. Now he has published more than twenty-five books.*

A poor response doesn't give details that help to explain what changed after the fifth novel.

Poor: *Mr. Spinelli wrote many novels. He kept getting rejected. After he sent in his fifth novel, publishers told him what was wrong with it. It was about a kid, and adults might not want to read about kids.*

Try It On Your Own

Directions: Read the passage. Then answer the questions that follow.

The Hunger Games Book Review

by Natasha Stark

The Hunger Games by Suzanne Collins is the most exciting book you will ever read. What makes it so good? The most obvious answer would be the unique plot. Set in North America in the future, Collins takes you to the 12 districts of Panem, where the ruling central government treats citizens without mercy. Every year, each district must provide a boy and girl between the ages of 12 to 18 to compete in the nationally-televised Hunger Games. The innocent teens are taken to the Capital where they are forced to fight to the death until only one player is left.

Suzanne Collins is an expert at creating cliff-hangers that leave you wanting more. Many plot twists and turns keep you on the edge of your chair. You have to keep reading until you've finished the book.

Perhaps another reason why this very unique plot appeals to readers is because it could almost be real. There is war in the world, and there are problems. Reality television shows are incredibly popular. All we need is a ruthless central government, and our future could be as deadly as the one in the book.

Another thing that makes the story exciting is the characters. Katniss Everdeen and Peeta Mellark face challenges every day. They live in one of the poorest districts; Katniss hunts illegally in order to feed her family. Since her father died while working in the mines, she has taken on the responsibility to protect her little sister and her mother. In fact, the reason that Katniss ends up in the Hunger Games is because she volunteers to compete in place of her little sister Primrose.

Collins does an outstanding job describing these characters, especially Katniss. Since the book is told from Katniss's perspective, we are inside her head and understand how she's feeling. By the end of the book, we know Katniss so well that we feel like we are her.

Young adults love the characters because we can relate to the struggles of Katniss and Peeta. Are we forced by the government to fight for our lives? No, but sometimes we do get tired of being told what to do. Do we have to make tough decisions? Yes. In many ways, we are no different from the characters in this book.

Suzanne Collins is truly an expert writer who knows how to entertain her readers. With a captivating plot and characters that young people can relate to, *The Hunger Games* is a must-read for anyone who loves to be challenged and entertained by a good book.

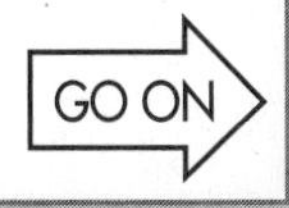

4 The writer supports her opinion that the book is exciting with two MAIN reasons. These reasons include—

A the unique plot and the interesting characters.
B the setting and the unique plot.
C the cliff-hangers and the characters.
D the descriptive writing and the realistic plot.

5 All the following is evidence used to support the idea that the plot is exciting and unique EXCEPT—

A innocent teens must fight to the death.
B the plot could almost be real.
C the book contains many cliff-hangers.
D the book is written from Katniss's perspective.

6 What evidence does the author give to support the idea that the characters make the book exciting? Give details or examples from the passage to support your answer. (3 points)

____

____

____

____

____

Test-Taking Tips

1 When choosing answers about similarities between selections, make sure that your choice is true for both selections.

2 When you want to find the order of events, look for signal words such as *first, then, tomorrow,* and *afterward*. Remember that events are not always given in the order in which they actually happened.

3 To find causes and effects, look for words and phrases such as *because, as a result,* and *so*. If there are no signal words, ask, "What caused this event?" or "What effect did this event have?"

4 For comparisons, look for words and phrases such as *like, same, but, unlike, on the other hand, instead of, rather than,* and *however.*

5 To answer questions about reasons and evidence, ask *Which fact or idea supports a specific point the writer is making?*

Go for it!

Unit Four Practice Test

Estimated time: 20 minutes

Directions: Read the following and then answer the questions that follow.

Inventions That Changed America: The Cotton Gin

Though he was not from the South and had no experience there until 1792, Eli Whitney created a machine that would completely change Southern agriculture. Because of him, cotton quickly became "king," or the most important crop, in the South. Also because of him—though this was certainly not his intention—the number of slaves greatly increased.

Eli's Bright Idea

1 Eli Whitney actually wanted to study to be a lawyer. He needed money, however, so he took a job as a tutor on a plantation in Georgia. He wasn't there long before he learned of the planters' problems with cotton. The only kind of cotton that could be grown inland, away from the coast, had sticky green seeds that were hard to separate from the cotton bolls, or capsules, which contain the fibers from which cloth and other cotton products are made. Until a way could be found to remove the seeds quickly, cotton crops could not make much money. Eli began to work on the problem. By spring of 1793, he had created the cotton engine, or "gin."

How the Cotton Gin Works

2 Eli's invention came in two sizes: a small version that could be hand cranked and a larger one that could run on water power or be harnessed to a horse. Either way, the idea was the same: Cotton bolls were fed into one end of the gin, where they caught on a revolving cylinder. The teeth on the cylinder pushed the cotton through narrow slots. Because cotton seeds were too large to fit through the slots, they fell to the floor of the machine. Then a rotating brush removed the cleaned cotton from the teeth on the cylinder and sent it out the other side of the gin.

Cotton as "King"

3 The development of the cotton gin had a great effect on the American economy. For one thing, the gin greatly increased the number of places where cotton could now be grown profitably. In 1800, only two states had significant cotton crops. By 1860, ten states did. The size of the 1860 crop was over 2 billion pounds, or more than 600 percent larger than the 1800 crop.

4 Cotton also became an increasingly important American export in the decades following the cotton gin's invention. In 1800, only 7 percent of the money made from exports came from cotton. By 1860, that number had increased to 57 percent. Much of the exported cotton was shipped to England, where it was made into cloth.

---

1 The author organized information in this article by—

A asking a question and then answering it.
B explaining how two things are alike.
C explaining how two things are different.
D presenting a problem and then a solution.

2 In paragraph 3, the writer states, "The development of the cotton gin had a great effect on the American economy." What evidence does the writer give to support this statement? (3 points)

____

____

____

____

____

Chapter 4

Copying Nature

1 Nature is full of amazing and useful objects. But when natural objects aren't practical to use, humans must invent their own. Throughout history, we have copied ideas from nature's plants and animals to make new inventions. Two interesting textiles—Velcro and fleece fabrics—were invented using ideas from nature.

Velcro

2 Have you ever walked through a field full of weeds? If there are cockleburs in that field, you'll bring some home with you. Cockleburs are weeds that stick to clothes.

3 In 1948, a Swiss man named George de Mestral found some cockleburs on his clothes and his dog. They were hard to pick off. He decided to find out why they were so pesky. He put one under a microscope. He saw many little burrs, or hooks, sticking out from the center. Those hooks helped the cocklebur grab and stick to fur and loops in fabric.

4 De Mestral thought that there must be a way to use this idea to make a fastener. He experimented for years. Then he finally did it! He found a way to make matching strips of fabric that hold tight like cockleburs but that come apart easily. One fabric strip had small fuzzy loops, and the other side had many small, stiff hooks like the cocklebur. When the two strips were pressed together, they held tightly, but they could also be pulled apart and reused.

5 De Mestral named his hook-and-loop fastener Velcro. The word is a combination of two words—velvet, a soft, plush fabric; and crochet, a type of needlework that uses a special hook to make a series of loops. Today, Velcro is often used instead of buttons, zippers, and laces. You can find it on shoes, on the International Space Station, and even in artificial hearts.

Fleece

6 The wool fleece from sheep is fluffy, warm, and soft. After a sheep is trimmed, the fleece grows back.

7 Polyester fleece was made to look like wool fleece, but large amounts of crude oil were used in the process. In 1993, textile makers discovered a way to save oil and make fleece fabrics. They used recycled plastic soda bottles!

8 Companies collect thousands of plastic bottles and chop them into tiny flakes. The flakes are cleaned, melted, and pushed through a spinneret to make long fibers.

9 Bales of fiber are sent to mills. There, the fibers are knit and dyed to make a soft, fluffy fabric. Synchilla and Polarfleece are two common names for this "recycled" fleece.

10 It takes 3,700 2-liter bottles to make enough Synchilla for 150 items of clothing. That's a lot of plastic. But that saves 42 gallons of crude oil and creates less air pollution.

11 Mountain-climbing clothes, hats, and jackets are made from these fleecy fabrics. They keep people warmer than real sheepskin and cost less.

12 Nature's own products often can't be beat. They have kept us comfortable and safe throughout our history. But copying nature to make new inventions often has surprisingly good results. Sometimes scientists can make a new product that is cheaper and even better than the natural one. These human-made products may help more people.

3 Read this sentence from the passage.

Throughout history, we have copied ideas from nature's plants and animals to make new inventions.

What evidence does the author give to support this point?

A Nature is full of amazing and useful objects.
B Sometimes things from the natural world aren't practical to use.
C George de Mestral copied cockleburs to invent Velcro.
D You can find Velcro in NASA space shuttles.

4 What was the problem with polyester fleece, and how did inventors solve this problem? Use details from the passage to support your answer. (3 points)

____

____

____

____

____

____

____

____

Directions: Use BOTH "Inventions That Changed America: The Cotton Gin" and "Copying Nature" to answer questions 5 through 8.

5 In both passages, the writers' point of view is that inventions—

A are unnecessary.
B improve life.
C cost too much.
D harm nature.

6 Which of these events happened first?

A The cotton gin was invented.
B Synchilla and Polarfleece were invented.
C Velcro was invented.
D Slavery increased.

7 How is the structure of "Copying Nature" different from "Inventions That Changed America: The Cotton Gin"?

A It gives examples of inventions that copy nature.
B It compares and contrasts Velcro and fleece.
C It explains how two inventions solved a problem in nature.
D It gives reasons that inventions fail.

8 One difference between the cotton gin and Velcro is that the cotton gin—

A was a new invention, but Velcro was not.
B was invented to change something found in nature, but Velcro was copying nature.
C ran on electricity, but Velcro doesn't.
D had only a small impact on American farmers, but Velcro has had a huge impact.

Points Earned/Total = _____/12

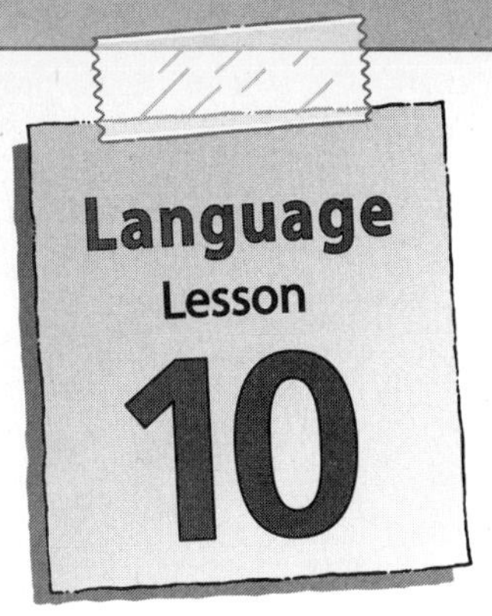

Verbs

Review the Standards (L.5.1.b, L.5.1.c, L.5.1.d)

- Use **perfect verb tenses** correctly
- Correct inappropriate **shifts** in verb tense

Q: How can I form and use **perfect verb tenses** correctly?

A: Use **perfect tense verbs** to communicate specific times when the action happened.

Present Perfect: A zebra has walked to this watering hole for years. (The zebra is still walking to the watering hole.)

I have drawn pictures of the zebra before. (At some time in the past, I drew a zebra.)

Past Perfect: The zebra had walked to this watering hole for years. (It used to walk, but now it isn't.)

Future Perfect: By the time the week is over, the zebra will have walked to the watering hole fifteen times. (The walking will take place before the week is over.)

Q: How do I find and correct **shifts** in verb tense?

A: When writing, make sure verbs agree, or are in the same tense.

Incorrect Shift: After I placed my money on the counter, the clerk gives me the candy.

Correct: After I placed my money on the counter, the clerk gave me the candy. (Both in past tense.)

Try It

Directions: Choose the correct verb tense for the following sentences.

1 Before I _____ to bed, I always brush my teeth.

A go
B went
C have gone
D am going

2 By the time the summer is over, I _____ thirty-five games of baseball.

A play
B played
C have played
D will have played

3 My grandmother _____ in this neighborhood since she was a little girl.

A lives
B has lived
C will live
D will have lived

Example 1 tests your understanding of **shifts in verb tense**. You must choose the verb that expresses the same tense as the verb *brush*. *Brush* is in present tense so you must choose the verb that is also in present tense. The correct answer is **choice A**, *go*.

Examples 2 and 3 test your knowledge of **perfect tense verbs**. Read the sentences carefully. Try substituting each verb into the blank and reading the sentence. **Example 2** is explaining how many games of baseball will have been played in the future. The correct verb is *will have played*, or **choice D**.

Example 3 is explaining an action that is still going on. The verb *has lived* is used to communicate an action that started in the past and is continuing into the present time. The correct answer is **choice B**, *has lived*.

Try It On Your Own

Directions: Choose the correct verb tense for the following sentences.

4 I didn't sleep last night because our neighbor's dog _____ all night!

A is barking
B barked
C will bark
D barks

5 Before I arrived, my little sister _____ her piano solo.

A plays
B will play
C will have played
D had played

6 Right now, I _____ to the kindergarteners.

A will be reading
B will read
C have read
D am reading

7 As I put on my coat and hat, my mom ____ me my lunch.

A gave
B gives
C will give
D has given

8 By the end of the school year, I _____ fifth grade.

A complete
B completed
C will complete
D will have completed

Conjunctions, Prepositions, and Interjections

Review the Standards (L.5.1.a, L.5.1.e, L.5.3.a)

- Explain **conjunctions, prepositions,** and **interjections**
- Use **correlative conjunctions**
- Expand, combine, and reduce sentences for meaning and style

Q: What are **prepositions** and **interjections**?

A: Prepositions show relationships between a noun or pronoun and another word in a sentence. They begin a group of words called a *prepositional phrase*.

Examples: Outside the window, a bird sang in the trees. (*Outside the window* and *in the trees* are prepositional phrases.)

An **interjection** is a word that expresses strong feeling.

Examples: Wow! That was a great kick!

Hey, your shoes are untied.

Q: What are **conjunctions** and **correlative conjunctions**?

A: Conjunctions such as *and, but, or, nor,* and *yet* connect groups of words. **Correlative conjunctions** are pairs of conjunctions that work together to connect ideas: *both/and, either/or, neither/nor.*

Example: My mom has been both a nurse and a teacher.

Use conjunctions and correlative conjunctions to combine sentences and make your writing flow smoothly.

Poor: The doctor couldn't figure out what was wrong with me. The nurse couldn't figure out what was wrong with me.

Good: Neither the doctor nor the nurse could figure out what was wrong with me.

Try It

Directions: Choose the best answer for each of the following questions.

1 What part of speech is the underlined word?

The name of the winner was announced yesterday.

A a conjunction
B a preposition
C an interjection
D a correlative conjunction

2 What part of speech is the underlined word?

I love reading science fiction, but I don't like fantasy.

A a conjunction
B a preposition
C a verb
D a correlative conjunction

3 Combine the following sentences using *either/or* as correlative conjunctions.

My mom will pick me up after the party. My dad might pick me up after the party too.

____

____

Example 1 asks you to identity the part of speech of the underlined word. Look at how *of* is used in the sentence. It begins a group of words—*of the winner.* You know that **prepositions** introduce groups of words and connect nouns with other words in the sentence. *Of* connects *winner* with the word *name.* The correct answer is **choice B.**

Example 2 asks you to identify the part of speech of the word *but.* The word *but* is connecting two groups of words in one sentence. It is a **conjunction**, or **choice A.**

For **Example 3**, you must use *either/or* as **correlative conjunctions** in a sentence.

Good: ***Either*** *my mom* **or** *my dad will pick me up after the party.*

Try It On Your Own

Directions: Choose the best answer for each of the following questions.

4 What part of speech is the underlined word?

Oops, I spilled chocolate milk on my computer!

A a conjunction
B a preposition
C an interjection
D a correlative conjunction

5 What parts of speech are the underlined words?

Although they are birds, neither the penguin nor the ostrich can fly.

A verbs
B prepositions
C interjections
D correlative conjunctions

6 Write a sentence using *or* as a conjunction.

____

____

____

7 Write a sentence using *to* as a preposition.

____

____

____

8 Read the paragraph.

> [1]Harriet Tubman helped hundreds of slaves escape from the South. [2]She helped them escape from the South during the Civil War. [3]She was a conductor on the Underground Railroad. [4]It was a secret network of safe houses where runaway slaves could hide on their way to freedom.

Which of the following BEST combines sentences 1 and 2?

A Harriet Tubman helped hundreds of slaves escape South from the Civil War.

B Harriet Tubman helped hundreds of slaves escape from the South she helped them during the Civil War.

C During the Civil War in the South, slaves escaped with Harriet Tubman.

D Harriet Tubman helped hundreds of slaves escape from the South during the Civil War.

Test-Taking Tips

1 When a question asks you to choose the correct verb, read the sentence silently with each possible verb. Often hearing the answer choices will help you decide when one is correct.

2 Remember that conjunctions (*and, but, or, yet*) join groups of words. A preposition begins a group of words that ends in a noun (*in bed, over the hill*). Interjections are words that show emotion (*Oh, Wow*).

3 Commas set off extra information in a sentence such as names, questions, and introductory words and groups of words. They are also used before a conjunction when two complete ideas are joined in one sentence.

Go for it!

Unit Five Practice Test

Estimated time: 18 minutes

Directions: Choose the best answer for the following questions.

1 What part of speech is the underlined word?

Oh, now I finally understand what you mean.

A preposition
B verb
C correlative conjunction
D interjection

2 What part of speech are the underlined words?

We didn't see either Juan or his little sister at the park.

A prepositions
B verbs
C correlative conjunctions
D interjections

3 What part of speech is the underlined word?

Without a flashlight, I couldn't see under the bed.

A preposition
B adverb
C correlative conjunction
D interjection

4 What part of speech is the underlined word?

I knew I couldn't win, yet I refused to give up.

A preposition
B conjunction
C correlative conjunction
D interjection

5 Write a sentence using an interjection. Underline the interjection. (1 point)

____

____

6 Write a sentence using *both / and* as correlative conjunctions.

____

____

7 Choose the correct verb for the sentence.

When we arrived at the store, it _____.

A is closed
B was closed
C is closing
D had been closed

8 Choose the correct verb for the sentence.

By the end of the hour, the artist _____ a sketch of the tree.

A is finishing
B will finish
C will have finished
D finished

9 Choose the correct verb for the sentence.

Until Galileo's observation of the planets, many people _____ that the Sun moves around the Earth.

A believe
B are believing
C had believed
D will have believed

10 Read the paragraph.

> [1]Alexis and I live on Frampton Street. [2]We have known each other for as long as I can remember. [3]Alexis has an older brother. [4]She has a baby sister. [5]Their names are Terrell and Keisha.

Which of the following BEST combines sentences 3 and 4?

A Alexis has an older brother or a baby sister.
B An older brother and a baby sister are what Alexis has.
C Alexis has an older brother, she has a baby sister too.
D Alexis has an older brother and a baby sister.

Points Earned/Total = _____/10

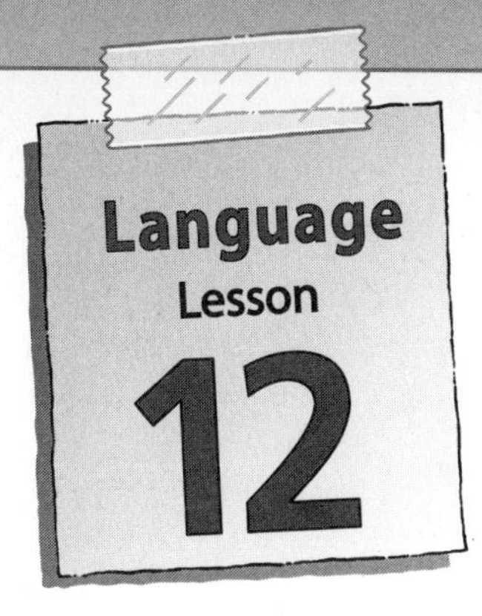

Unit Six—Capitalization, Punctuation, and Spelling

Commas

Review the Standards (L.5.2, L.5.2.a, L.5.2.b, L.5.2.c)

- Use correct **capitalization** and punctuation
- Use punctuation to separate **items in a series**
- Use **commas** after introductory elements, tag questions, and direct address

Q: What words should be **capitalized**?

A: Capitalize the first word of every sentence, the pronoun *I*, titles of people and works, and nouns and pronouns that refer to specific people, places, and things (proper nouns and adjectives).

Examples: My Aunt Maggie and I went to Washington, D.C., to visit The Smithsonian Museum of Natural History.

Q: When do I use **commas**?

A: **Commas** are used to separate items in a series or to separate words from the rest of the sentence.

Items in a Series: We painted the doors, window frames, and shutters.

Introductory Elements: Although it looks challenging, I still want to go.

Tag Questions: You caught the ball, didn't you?

Direct Address: Alexis, have you finished your work?

Q: What other punctuation is used to separate **items in a series**?

A: Colons and semicolons can also be used to separate **items in a series**.

Colons are sometimes used to introduce a list. Often, a colon comes after the phrase *the following*.

Example: Please remember to bring the following: a sleeping bag, a change of clothes, and a flashlight.

Semicolons can be used to separate items that have commas.

Example: I have lived in Boise, Idaho; Houston, Texas; and Hollywood, California.

Try It

Directions: Answer the following questions.

1 Which of the following sentences is punctuated correctly?

A She isn't my sister but, she is my cousin.
B This year I'm playing soccer baseball, and basketball.
C Yes I will be, running the race.
D That's your mom's car, isn't it?

2 Which sentence is punctuated correctly?

A Mr. Lee builds houses does home repairs and installs fences.
B All of the following may be found in your desks: pencils, pens, rulers, paper, and note cards.
C This summer we visited Helena, Montana Salt Lake City, Utah and Reno, Nevada.
D The following students should report to the office; Jimmy Chou, Sandra Ramirez, and Zane Jackson.

3 Which sentence is punctuated correctly?

A Mr. Lee builds houses in the summer; he does home repairs in the winter.
B Mr. Lee has many roles; carpenter, plumber, painter, electrician.
C Mr. Lee built the house; at 27 Larkspur Road in Greenville.
D When he sells real estate; he works for the Prime Spot Company.

4 Which sentence uses correct capitalization?

A My uncle races Stock Cars as a hobby.
B He lives near cresco, iowa.
C On the weekends, he races cars at the Howard County Fairgrounds.
D I'm going to watch him this sunday.

For **Example 1**, you must think about the rules for **commas**. Commas are used to separate items in a series, introductory words, and tag questions. They are also used before a conjunction in compound sentences. Only choice D has a comma correctly placed before a tag question. The correct answer is **choice D**.

Each of the choices in **Example 2** contains items in a series. You must think about which list is correctly punctuated. Read through the choices, eliminating the choices which you immediately know are incorrect. Choice A is missing commas. Choice C has commas, but needs semicolons between the items with commas. Choice D has a semicolon instead of a colon before a list. The only correct sentence is **choice B**.

Example 3 asks about a specific punctuation mark—the **semicolon**. The semicolon is used in a compound sentence that does not use a conjunction (*and, or,* or *but)* to join the two complete thoughts. In choice B, a colon should be used instead of the semicolon to indicate a list. In choice C, no punctuation is needed after the word *house*. And choice D

comma after *real estate* to set off the introductory phrase, *When he sells real estate.* Thus, **choice A** is correct because a semicolon is used correctly to separate two sentences.

Example 4 tests your knowledge of **capitalization.** Specific people, places, and things should be capitalized. This means that *Stock Cars* should not be capitalized in choice A, but *Cresco, Iowa,* and *Sunday* should be capitalized in choices B and D. Choice C capitalizes a specific place. **Choice C** is correct.

◎ Try It On Your Own

Directions: Answer the following questions.

5 Which of the following is correctly punctuated?

A Lenny had to buy three things: milk, bread, and juice.
B Lenny had to buy three things; milk, bread, and juice.
C Lenny had to buy three things, milk, bread, and juice.
D Lenny had to buy three: things milk, bread, and juice.

6 Which of the following is correctly punctuated?

A Lenny came back three hours later: but he had forgotten the groceries.
B Lenny came back three hours later; but he had forgotten the groceries.
C Lenny came back three hours later, but he had forgotten the groceries.
D Lenny came back three hours later but, he had forgotten the groceries.

7 Which of the following is correctly punctuated?

A Although it was raining we still managed to gather wood, to start a fire, and to cook hot dogs.
B Although it was raining, we still managed, to gather wood, to start a fire, and to cook hot dogs.
C Although it was raining, we still managed to gather wood start a fire and cook hot dogs.
D Although it was raining, we still managed to gather wood, to start a fire, and to cook hot dogs.

8 All of the following sentences use commas correctly EXCEPT which one?

A Is that you, Tyrell?
B No, I won't be at school tomorrow.
C It's raining so, I don't want to go to the park.
D May I have a glass of water, please?

9 Which of the following sentences correctly uses capitalization?

A Please give the instructions to dr. Hardy-Smith.
B Do you like indian food?
C I attend Jackson elementary school.
D My mom took me to the Metropolitan Museum of Art.

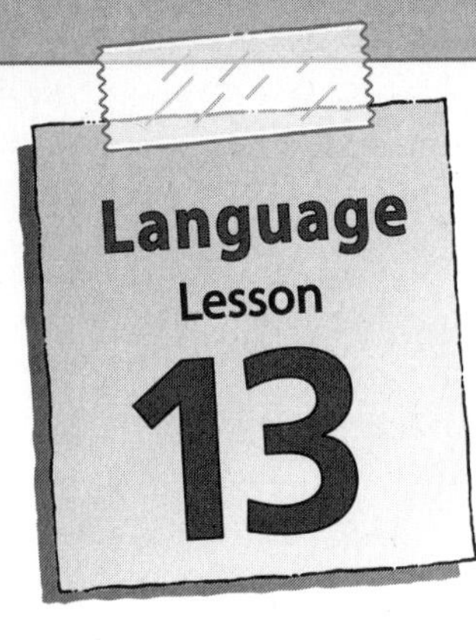

Titles and Spelling

Review the Standards (L.5.2.d, L.5.2.e)

- Use underlining, quotation marks, or italics with **titles of works**
- **Spell** words correctly

Q: What are the rules for capitalizing and punctuating **titles of works**?

A: Capitalize the first word, the last word, and all important words in the titles of books, newspapers, short stories, plays, and works of art such as paintings.

Italics (or underlining) are used with the following titles: books, magazines, newspapers, plays, movies, and works of art.

Examples: the *New York Times*, *Sports Illustrated,* the *Mona Lisa*, *Maniac McGee*

Quotation marks are used with titles of smaller works such as book chapters, short stories, poems, articles, and songs.

Examples: "Casey at the Bat," "The Star Spangled Banner," "The Mets Great Comeback"

Q: What are common **spelling** mistakes I can avoid?

A: Some of the most common spelling mistakes involve homophones, or words that sound alike but have different spellings and meanings. Make sure you know the meaning and spelling of the following homophones.

There/their/they're	through/threw	whose/who's
Its/it's	weak/week	our/hour

 **Try It**

Directions: Read each question and choose the best answer.

1 Which of the following titles is correct?

A the book To Kill a Mockingbird

B the poem *Sick* by Shel Silverstein

C "Seventeen" magazine

D the sculpture *David* by Michaelangelo

2 In which of the following sentences are the titles correctly punctuated?

A The song "Smells Like Teen Spirit" is on the album "Nevermind" by Nirvana.

B My brother has the lead role in the one-act play Romeo and Julie.

C One of my favorite horse movies is "Secretariat."

D Did you read the chapter A God Buys Us Cheeseburgers from *The Lightning Thief*?

3 Complete the sentence by choosing the correct spelling of the word.

A lion will roar _____ when it is angry.

A fiercely

B feircely

C fearcely

D feersley

4 In which sentence is the underlined word NOT spelled correctly?

A He wore a belt around his waist.

B The book is on the fourth shelf.

C She goes to dance class every week.

D The ball went threw the window.

Example 1 tests your knowledge of how to write **titles**. Remember that magazine and book titles are underlined or italicized, so choices A and C are incorrect. Shorter works or parts of works are put in quotation marks. Choice B is incorrect. However, works of art such as paintings and sculptures are italicized (or underlined.) **Choice D** is correct.

To answer **Example 2**, look closely at each sentence. Some sentences have two titles in them. Shorter works such as songs and chapters require quotation marks. Longer works need italics or underlining. Only **choice B** correctly underlines a play title.

Example 3 asks you to choose the correct spelling of a word. **Choice A** is correct. The other three choices illustrate common spelling errors.

Example 4 tests your ability to choose the correctly spelled **homophone**. Homophones are words that sound the same but have different spellings and meanings. In order to choose the correct homophone, you need to learn the meaning associated with each spelling of the word. In this example, the first three choices use the homophones correctly. Choice D does not use the correct homophone. The word *threw* is the past tense of the word *throw* and means "tossed." The correct homophone to use in this sentence is *through.* The correct answer is **choice D**.

Try It On Your Own

Directions: Read each question and choose the best answer.

5 Which of the following sentences uses correct punctuation and capitalization?

A Have you read *the Invention of Hugo Cabret*?

B The magazine "Publisher's Weekly" said that the book was a masterpiece.

C Brian Selznick also wrote the book "The Houdini Box."

D The movie based upon the book is simply called *Hugo*.

6 Which of the following sentences uses correct punctuation and capitalization?

A I recently visited the art institute of Chicago in Illinois.

B I wanted to see the painting American Gothic.

C I also wanted to see the museum's display of tiny rooms described in the book *The Sixty-Eight Rooms*.

D I read about the rooms in our newspaper The Dallas Morning News.

7 Which word is spelled correctly?

A begining

B wierd

C alot

D knowledge

8 Complete the sentence by choosing the correct spelling of the word.

_______ is no time like the present to do an outstanding job.

A There

B They're

C Their

D They are

Test-Taking Tips

1 Spelling questions often test you over homophones, or words that sound the same but have different spellings and meanings. Ask yourself, *Does this spelling fit the meaning of the word?*

2 In general, shorter works (poems, chapters, articles) are placed in quotation marks, while longer works (books, magazines, newspapers) are italicized or underlined.

3 Be sure to read the question carefully. Make sure you understand whether you need to identify the CORRECT or INCORRECT sentence.

Go for it!

Unit Six Practice Test

Estimated time: 15 minutes

1 Complete the sentence by choosing the correct spelling of the word.

The movie star made a surprise _____.

A apearrance
B appearrance
C appearance
D apeerance

2 In which sentence is the underlined word NOT spelled correctly?

A The nurse is in charge of six patience.
B He just bought a new pair of sneakers.
C That box of cereal has already been opened.
D Putting on a bandage will help your cut heal.

3 Which title is INCORRECT?

A the television show *American Idol*
B the song *Ten Thousand Fireflies*
C the magazine *American Girl*
D the painting *The Scream*

4 Read the sentence and choose the correct verb.

By 1 o'clock, three hundred students _____ lunch.

A eat
B will eat
C have eaten
D will have eaten

5 Which of the following sentences is correct?

A Please send these pictures to the following students: Mara Gomez, Cynthia Hardy, Mike Harper, and Lee Tauo.
B I've visited: Eugene Oregon, Detroit Michigan, and Los Angeles California.
C For Thanksgiving we usually feast on corn bread, turkey, mashed potatoes and black-eyed peas.
D James agreed to do the following clean the garage, wash the car, and mow the lawn.

6 Which sentence is punctuated correctly?

A “I want to come with you,” said Jesse.
B The corn grew slowly at first now, it is seven feet high.
C Tom wants to play baseball; but Tony wants to play basketball.
D At the picnic, we had corn; hot dogs; and hamburgers.

7 Which sentence is punctuated correctly?

A Next Saturday is Uncle Petes birthday.
B We will go to the house on Peach St for his party.
C “What are you bringing for a gift? my sister asked.”
D I told her I was giving him a T-shirt, some socks, and tickets to the ball game.

8 Complete the sentence by choosing the correct spelling of the word.

Who took _____ place in line?

A hour
B our
C are
D how’re

Points Earned/Total = _____/8

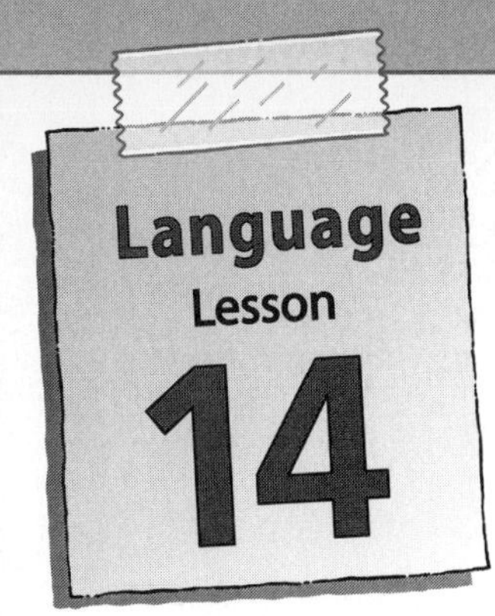

Word Meanings

Review the Standards (RI.5.4.a, L.5.4.a, L.5.4.c, L.5.5.c)

- Use **context clues** to find the meaning of a word or phrase
- Use **dictionaries**, **glossaries**, and **thesauruses** to find the pronunciation and meanings of words
- Use **synonyms**, **antonyms**, and **homographs**

Q: How can **context clues** help me find the meaning of a word?

A: **Context clues** are the other words in a sentence or nearby sentences that help you understand an unfamiliar word. This chart describes some common types of context clues you may encounter while reading.

Context Clue	Example
Definition	The leaves will decay, or rot.
Example	The building was rustic, like a farmhouse hundreds of years ago.
Restatement	His scheme was a plan that could never work.
Compare/Contrast	He was not warm and kind, but ruthless.

Q: How can I use **dictionaries**, **glossaries**, and **thesauruses** to understand new words?

A: A **glossary** is usually found in the back of a book and explains words found in the book. A **thesaurus** gives synonyms and antonyms of often-used words. A **dictionary** is the most complete resource to use when looking for information on new words. It lists all of the possible meanings, the parts of speech, and the pronunciation of words.

Q: What are **synonyms**, **antonyms**, and **homographs**?

A: **Synonyms** are words that mean almost the same thing: smart/intelligent.

Antonyms are words that mean the opposite: hot/cold.

Homographs are words that are spelled the same but have different meanings: The word *bear* can mean an animal or "to support or carry."

Directions: Read the passage. Then answer the questions that follow.

from The Secret Garden

by Frances Hodgson Burnett

1 Mary sat up in bed and felt miserable and angry.

2 "The rain is as contrary as I ever was," she said. "It came because it knew I did not want it."

3 She threw herself back on her pillow and buried her face. . . . She had been lying awake turning from side to side for about an hour, when suddenly something made her sit up in bed and turn her head toward the door listening. She listened and she listened. . . .

4 The door of her room was ajar and the sound came down the corridor, a far-off faint sound of fretful crying. She listened for a few minutes and each minute she became more and more sure. She felt as if she must find out what it was . . . Perhaps the fact that she was in a rebellious mood made her bold. She put her foot out of bed and stood on the floor. . . .

5 There was a candle by her bedside and she took it up and went softly out of the room. The corridor looked very long and dark, but she was too excited to mind that. She thought she remembered the corners she must turn to find the short corridor with the door covered with tapestry. . . . The sound had come up that passage. So she went on with her dim light, almost feeling her way, her heart beating so loud that she fancied she could hear it. The far-off faint crying went on and led her. Sometimes it stopped for a moment or so and then began again. Was this the right corner to turn? She stopped and thought. Yes, it was. Down this passage and then to the left, and then up two broad steps, and then to the right again. Yes, there was the tapestry door.

6 She pushed it open very gently and closed it behind her, and she stood in the corridor and could hear the crying quite plainly, though it was not loud. It was on the other side of the wall at her left and a few yards farther on there was a door. She could see a glimmer of light coming from beneath it. The Someone was crying in that room, and it was quite a young Someone.

7 So she walked to the door and pushed it open. . . .

8 It was a big room with ancient, handsome furniture in it. There was a low fire glowing faintly on the hearth and a night-light burning by the side of a carved four-poster bed hung with brocade, and on the bed was lying a boy, crying fretfully . . . The boy had a sharp, delicate face the color of ivory and he seemed to have eyes too big for it. He had also a lot of hair which tumbled over his forehead in heavy locks and made his thin face seem smaller. He looked like a boy who had been ill, but he was crying more as if he were tired and cross than as if he were in pain.

1 As used in paragraph 4, rebellious means—

A illegal.
B careful.
C nervous and uneasy.
D disobedient.

2 Read the dictionary entry.

> **lock** *n.* **1.** fastening operated by a key **2.** enclosure used to raise and lower boats in a canal **3.** ringlet of hair *v.* **4.** to fasten or make secure

Which definition BEST fits the way lock is used in paragraph 8?

A definition 1
B definition 2
C definition 3
D definition 4

3 Which word is a synonym for fretful?

A cheerful
B unhappy
C noisy
D excited

For **Example 1**, you must use **context clues** to help you determine the meaning of the word *rebellious*. From the context, you understand that Mary must find out what the noise is. She is feeling bold. The answer is **choice D**.

Example 2 asks you to use a **dictionary** entry to find the definition of an unknown word. Using both the context and the dictionary, you can determine that the *lock* in the story is a ringlet of hair. The correct answer is **choice C**.

Example 3 asks you to choose a **synonym** for the word *fretful*. Remember that a synonym is a word that has a similar meaning. From the context, you can conclude that *fretful* describes the crying Mary hears. You also know the crying is not loud. Together these clues help you decide that the synonym for *fretful* is *unhappy*, or **choice B**.

Try It On Your Own

4 Reread this sentence from the passage.

She thought she remembered the corners she must turn to find the short corridor with the door covered with tapestry. . . . The sound had come up that passage.

Which word in the sentence is a restatement of the word corridor?

A *corners*
B *short*
C *covered*
D *passage*

5 Which word is an antonym for ajar?

A closed
B open
C container
D thick

6 In this story, the homophone cross means—

A in a bad mood.
B to move across.
C a shape made by two overlapping lines.
D to go against.

7 From the context, you know that a hearth is—

A a type of bed.
B an illness.
C a little boy
D part of a fireplace.

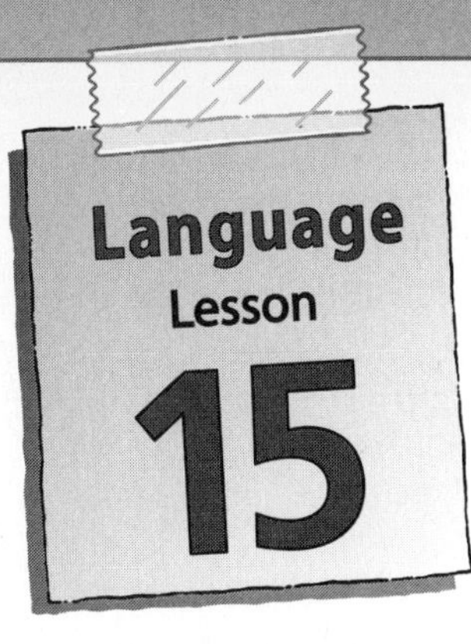

Word Parts and Relationships

Review the Standards (L.5.4.b, L.5.6)

- Use **prefixes**, **suffixes**, and **roots** to determine word meaning
- Understand **academic words**

Q: How can I use **prefixes**, **suffixes**, and **roots** to determine word meanings?

A: **Prefixes** are word parts added to the beginning of a **root**, or base, word. **Suffixes** are word parts added to the end of a root word. Knowing the meaning of common prefixes, suffixes, and roots will help you figure out new words.

Prefix	Meaning	Example
dis-	opposite, lack of	dishonorable (without honor)
im-	not, opposite of	impossible (not possible)
inter-	between, among, together	international (between or among nations)
mis-	bad, badly	misfortune (bad fortune)
pre-	before	prewar (before war)
sub-	under, below, lower	subnormal (below normal)

Suffix	Meaning	Example
-able	able to be, suitable for	manageable (able to be managed)
-er	more, one who does	follower (one who follows)
-less	without	meatless (without meat)
-ly	in a manner	cheerfully (in a cheerful manner)
-ment	act or state of	enjoyment (act of enjoying)
-ness	state or quality of	greatness (state of being great)
-ous	full of	joyous (full of joy)

Q: What are **academic words**?

A: **Academic words** are words that are commonly used in books you read at school. Some academic words are mainly used in certain subjects. For example, the words *habitat, theory,* and *environment* are academic words used in science books. Some academic words are used to show relationships between ideas, such as *however* (a contrast), *similarly* (the same), and *in addition* (builds upon a previous idea).

Try It

Directions: Read the passage. Then answer the questions that follow.

Fleeting Masterpieces

1 They are beautiful but impermanent works of art. Found on mud walls in villages of West Africa, they are some of the world's most dazzling wall paintings. Few people outside the villages will ever see them, however. Most of these colorful paintings are washed away during the rainy season.

2 Women from countries such as Mauritania, Ghana, and Nigeria create these fleeting masterpieces. They use pigments, or colors, that come from local plants and clays. Their painting tools are simple: a clay bowl to hold the colored paste and a spoon handle or homemade brush to outline designs. With their bare hands, the women apply paint to large areas. The patterns they create are bold, bright, and meaningful, each telling something significant about the life of its maker. For instance, the painting might show a cooking pot, or it might repeat the pattern from a traditional cloth.

3 Most of these paintings are found on the outside walls of the village houses. However, some women of the Sominke tribe in Mauritania paint on the inside of their houses because they spend so much time there. These women's villages are located on the edge of the Sahara Desert, where temperatures can reach 120°F by noon. The paintings provide welcome beauty in the harsh desert surroundings.

4 Sadly, the tradition of making wall paintings is disappearing. For generations, mothers taught the skill to their daughters. Now, however, many younger women are not interested in learning old traditions. We can only hope that this unique and beautiful art form will survive for generations to come.

1 Reread this sentence from paragraph 1.

They are beautiful but impermanent works of art.

Adding the prefix *im-* to the root *permanent* creates a new word that means—

A before permanent.

B state of being permanent.

C not permanent.

D permanent again.

2 Read the following sentences from the first paragraph.

. . . they are some of the world's most dazzling wall paintings. Few people outside the villages will ever see them, however.

The word however indicates that the information in the second sentence is—

A the same as in the first sentence.

B different from the first sentence.

C an effect of the ideas in the first sentence.

D restating the ideas in the first sentence.

3 In paragraph 4, the word tradition refers to a—

A way of doing things passed from older to younger people.

B religious holiday.

C story about the past.

D village in West Africa.

To answer **Example 1**, you must use your knowledge of **roots**, **prefixes**, and **suffixes** to determine the meaning of *impermanent.* Prefixes are word parts added to the beginning of a root, or base, word. Suffixes are word parts added to the end of a root word. The prefix *im-*, which means "not" or "opposite of," has been added to the root word *permanent.* The word *impermanent*, then, means "not permanent." **Choice C** is correct.

Example 2 asks you to think about the meaning of the **academic word** *however.* In this case, *however* shows a contrast between the beautiful paintings and the fact that they will not be seen by many people. The correct answer is **choice B**.

For **Example 3**, you must define the academic word *tradition.* You have probably seen this word in social studies or history books. A close look at how the word is used in this passage reveals that a tradition is something passed down from mother to daughter or generation to generation. The correct answer is **choice A**.

Try It On Your Own

Directions: Use "Fleeting Masterpieces" to answer the questions that follow.

4 Based upon the suffix *–ful*, the word meaningful means—

A having no meaning.

B full of meaning.

C one who creates meaning.

D a state of meaning.

5 Based upon the suffix *-er*, a *maker* is—

A one who creates a painting.
B a greater person in the village.
C a younger daughter.
D a brush used for painting.

6 From the last sentence of paragraph 4, you understand that the word generations is referring to—

A a group of people who will live in future.
B people who collect art.
C tribes in Africa.
D a type of pigment that comes from plants.

Test-Taking Tips

1 Context clues may not be in the same sentence as the unknown word. Sometimes clues are in the surrounding sentences.

2 If you cannot figure out the meaning of a word from its root, suffix, or prefix, look at the answer choices carefully. See which one makes the most sense in the context of the sentence and passage.

3 When looking for antonyms (opposites), don't be fooled by choices that actually mean the same thing (synonyms).

Go for it!

Unit Seven Practice Test

Estimated time: 20 minutes

Directions: Read the passage. Then answer the questions that follow.

1 Today, Americans devour over 9 million tons of tomatoes a year. But in **colonial** times, Americans refused to eat them. They considered the tomato poisonous because it belonged to a family of deadly plants. Tomatoes were not mentioned at all in the first American cookbooks.

2 Europeans were faster to welcome the tomato into their diet. By the 1700s, tomatoes were popular in Italy, Portugal, and other countries near the Mediterranean Sea. American sailors who visited these lands enjoyed eating tomatoes and may have spread the word about them when they returned home. But most Americans still needed to be convinced that tomatoes were edible. Thomas Jefferson was one of the first Americans to raise tomatoes in his garden. He may have enjoyed tasting its sweet red flesh, but few of his fellow citizens were ready to join him.

3 Some historians say that in 1820 a well-known farmer in Salem County, New Jersey, may have calmed America's fears. Robert Gibbon Johnson bravely ate a tomato on the Salem courthouse steps, shocking the crowd when he did not die. Two decades later, however, some Americans were still cautious. One 1840s cookbook recommended boiling a tomato for three hours to get rid of its "raw taste."

4 By the late 1890s, Americans no longer mistrusted the tomato. Indeed, it was rapidly becoming popular. *The Book of Good Dinners for My Friend*, a Boston cookbook of the **era**, included numerous recipes for tomatoes. It taught Americans how to broil, stuff, and fry tomatoes, as well as make tomato salad, sauce, and soup.

5 Over 100 years later, the "poisonous" tomato is a staple of the American diet. We now know that fresh tomatoes are not only good-tasting, but very nutritious. They are low in calories, are a good source of **fiber**, and are high in vitamins A and C. They also contain the substance **lycopene**, which may help prevent certain forms of cancer.

www.photos.com

1 In paragraph 1, the word devour means—

A to throw away.
B to grow.
C to eat eagerly.
D to sell.

2 Which word from the passage has a suffix that means "full of"?

A *poisonous*
B *tasting*
C *edible*
D *rapidly*

3 Study this glossary.

Glossary

colonial	Having to do with the 13 British colonies that became the United States of America.
era	Period of time marked by distinctive events.
fiber	Part of a plant that is wholly or partially indigestible when eaten.
lycopene	Red substance found in the blood, the reproductive organs, tomatoes, and palm oils; may help lower the risk of prostate cancer.

Which word refers to the time period of the British colonies in America?

A colonial
B era
C fiber
D lycopene

4 Reread this sentence from paragraph 5.

Over 100 years later, the "poisonous" tomato is a staple of the American diet.

Which sentence uses the word staple to mean the same thing?

A I will staple the pages together.
B Mom bought eggs, milk, and other staples.
C The teacher needed tape and staples.
D The tiny staple is made of wire.

5 The word <u>edible</u> means—

A able to be grown.
B having to do with tomatoes.
C able to be eaten.
D having to do with sailing.

6 Knowing that the Latin root *nat* means "born" helps you understand that a plant *native* to an area is one that—

A must be brought from another place.
B can cause death.
C is eaten only by babies.
D grows there originally.

7 Reread this sentence from paragraph 4.

By the late 1890s, Americans no longer <u>mistrusted</u> the tomato.

Adding the prefix *mis-* to the word *trusted* creates a new word that means—

A in a trusted way.
B not trusted.
C trusted once.
D trusted before.

8 What is a synonym for the word <u>cautious</u>, as it is used in paragraph 3?

A shocked
B calm
C careful
D amused

9 Read the thesaurus entry.

SWEET
adjective
synonyms: sugary, syrupy, lovable, pleasant
antonyms: bitter, sour

Which word means the opposite of <u>sweet</u>?

A sour
B pleasant
C syrupy
D sugary

10 Read the dictionary entry.

> **raise** (rāz) *v.* **1.** to lift up **2.** to cause to rise **3.** to increase in amount **4.** to help to grow.

Which definition BEST fits the way raise is used in paragraph 2?

A definition 1
B definition 2
C definition 3
D definition 4

Points Earned/Total = _____/10

This test will tell you how well you understand the Common Core State Standards **after** using this book.

Mastery Test: Part 1

Estimated time: 50 minutes

Directions: Read the following passage. Then answer the questions that follow.

Perry Moves In

Perry stepped into the elevator with his arms full of boxes. He tried to whistle, but the lump in his throat was in his way. An older man stood in the back of the elevator. He looked curiously at Perry.

"So, you are new in this apartment building?" the man asked.

Perry blinked back a tear and nodded. "My mom and I just moved to the city," he said.

"I, too, moved when I was your age," the man said in heavily accented English. "Imagine, I had never been outside the village before. I had never even seen a car. Suddenly I am in land of buildings like . . . like mountains. I almost—"

The elevator doors slid open at the 26th floor. "This is your floor, yes?" the man said, gallantly helping Perry out.

Perry walked down the hall, wondering about the man. What was his name? What country was he from? And what was he about to say when the elevator doors opened? Perry thought about the old man as he unpacked. The next day, Perry ran into the man in the lobby of the building. When he saw Perry, he started in with his story as if no time at all had passed.

"As I say, I almost jumped off the boat and swam back to the village," the man continued. "I feel I cannot live in the city of smoke and noise."

Perry smiled. He knew about those kinds of feelings.

"So rude—I have not told you my name!" the man exclaimed. "I am Aldo, but the friends call me Al." Al solemnly exchanged introductions with Perry, then continued talking until Perry had to leave. From then on, Al told more about his life every time he saw Perry around the building. Sometimes Perry even searched around the building until he ran into Al. Al talked about coming from Italy to help his father run a fruit-and-vegetable stand.

One day Perry brought a new friend home from school. The boys ran into Al on the elevator. When Perry took his dog out for a walk the next morning, he met Al on the sidewalk outside the building. Al asked, "You and your friend have fun, yes?"

"We had a great time," Perry answered. "But I want to hear more of your stories."

"No more stories to tell," Al said.

"Sure there are," Perry insisted. "I never learned what happened after the horse ate your father's apples."

Al put his hand on Perry's shoulder. "You have been kind to hear this old man talk. I saw you were lonely, and I tell myself, even foolish stories are better than sad heart. Now you have friends. You are happy. You don't need these stories anymore."

"I may not *need* to hear them, but I want to hear them—more than you can know," Perry said softly.

1 We can infer that Perry's main problem is that he—

A is old.
B is lonely.
C cannot speak English.
D misses Italy.

2 How does Al help Perry? Support your answer using evidence from the passage. (3 points)

3 What is a theme of this passage?

A Friends may be found in the most unexpected places.
B Kids are more interesting than elderly people.
C A big city is a dangerous place to live.
D Running a fruit-and-vegetable stand is rewarding.

4 How does Al feel at the end of the story? Support your answer using a direct quotation from the story. (3 points)

5 Write a summary of the passage. (3 points)

____

____

____

____

____

____

Directions: Read the following passage. Then answer the questions that follow.

from Anne of Green Gables

In the following excerpt, Matthew Cuthbert goes to pick up an orphan boy whom he and his sister Marilla are taking into their home. However, when he arrives he finds that the orphanage has sent a little girl instead.

Matthew, however, was spared the ordeal of speaking first, for as soon as she [Anne] concluded that he was coming to her she stood up, grasping with one thin brown hand the handle of a shabby, old-fashioned carpet-bag; the other she held out to him.

"I suppose you are Mr. Matthew Cuthbert of Green Gables?" she said in a peculiarly clear, sweet voice. "I'm very glad to see you. I was beginning to be afraid you weren't coming for me and I was imagining all the things that might have happened to prevent you. I had made up my mind that if you didn't come for me tonight I'd go down the track to that big wild cherry-tree at the bend, and climb up into it to stay all night. I wouldn't be a bit afraid, and it would be lovely to sleep in a wild cherry-tree all white with bloom in the moonshine, don't you think? You could imagine you were dwelling in marble halls, couldn't you? And I was quite sure you would come for me in the morning, if you didn't tonight."

Matthew had taken the scrawny little hand awkwardly in his; then and there he decided what to do. He could not tell this child with the glowing eyes that there had been a mistake; he would take her home and let Marilla do that. She couldn't be left at Bright River anyhow, no matter what mistake had been made, so all questions and explanations might as well be deferred until he was safely back at Green Gables.

"I'm sorry I was late," he said shyly. "Come along. The horse is over in the yard. Give me your bag."

"Oh, I can carry it," the child responded cheerfully. "It isn't heavy. I've got all my worldly goods in it, but it isn't heavy. And if it isn't carried in just a certain way the handle pulls out—so I'd better keep it because I know the exact knack of it. It's an extremely old carpet-bag. Oh, I'm very glad you've come,

even if it would have been nice to sleep in a wild cherry-tree. We've got to drive a long piece, haven't we? Mrs. Spencer said it was eight miles. I'm glad because I love driving. Oh, it seems so wonderful that I'm going to live with you and belong to you. I've never belonged to anybody—not really . . . They were good, you know—the asylum people. But there is so little scope for the imagination in an asylum—only just in the other orphans. It was pretty interesting to imagine things about them—to imagine that perhaps the girl who sat next to you was really the daughter of a belted earl, who had been stolen away from her parents in her infancy by a cruel nurse who died before she could confess. I used to lie awake at nights and imagine things like that, because I didn't have time in the day. I guess that's why I'm so thin—I *am* dreadful thin, ain't I? There isn't a pick on my bones. I do love to imagine I'm nice and plump, with dimples in my elbows."

With this Matthew's companion stopped talking, partly because she was out of breath and partly because they had reached the buggy. Not another word did she say until they had left the village . . . The child put out her hand and broke off a branch of wild plum that brushed against the side of the buggy.

"Isn't that beautiful? What did that tree, leaning out from the bank, all white and lacy, make you think of?" she asked.

"Well now, I dunno," said Matthew.

"Why, a bride, of course—a bride all in white with a lovely misty veil. I've never seen one, but I can imagine what she would look like. I don't ever expect to be a bride myself. I'm so homely nobody will ever want to marry me . . . Oh, there are a lot more cherry-trees all in bloom! This Island is the bloomiest place. I just love it already, and I'm so glad I'm going to live here. I've always heard that Prince Edward Island was the prettiest place in the world, and I used to imagine I was living here, but I never really expected I would. It's delightful when your imaginations come true, isn't it?"

"Well now, I dunno," said Matthew.

"Isn't it splendid to think of all the things there are to find out about? It just makes me feel glad to be alive—it's such an interesting world. It wouldn't be half so interesting if we know all about everything, would it? There'd be no scope for imagination then, would there? But am I talking too much? People are always telling me I do. Would you rather I didn't talk? If you say so I'll stop. I can *stop* when I make up my mind to it, although it's difficult."

Matthew, much to his own surprise, was enjoying himself. Like most quiet folks he liked talkative people when they were willing to do the talking themselves and did not expect him to keep up his end of it. But he had never expected to enjoy the society of a little girl . . . he thought that he "kind of liked her chatter." So he said as shyly as usual:

"Oh, you can talk as much as you like. I don't mind."

6 Which of the following best describes Anne?

A shy

B imaginative

C fearful

D generous

7 How does Matthew decide to handle the problem of finding Anne at the station instead of the boy they expected?

A He decides to leave her at the station.
B He puts her on a train back to the orphanage.
C He takes her for a ride in his buggy.
D He takes her home and lets his sister Marilla fix the problem.

8 From the context of the passage, you can infer that an asylum is a—

A home for orphans.
B hospital.
C school.
D farm.

9 Which of the following words found in the passage are antonyms?

A *chatter/shyly*
B *quiet/talkative*
C *thin/dimples*
D *scrawny/glowing*

10 Which of the following phrases explains Matthew's point of view of the events in the story?

A *With this Matthew's companion stopped talking, partly because she was out of breath . . .*
B *I guess that's why I'm so thin—I am dreadful thin, ain't I?*
C *Like most quiet folks he liked talkative people when they were willing to do the talking themselves . . .*
D *Matthew had taken the scrawny little hand awkwardly in his . . .*

Use both "Perry Moves In" and *Anne of Green Gables* to answer the following questions.

11 Which of the following characters speaks with an Italian accent?

A Matthew
B Perry
C Aldo
D Anne

12 Which of the following would go under **Both** in the diagram?

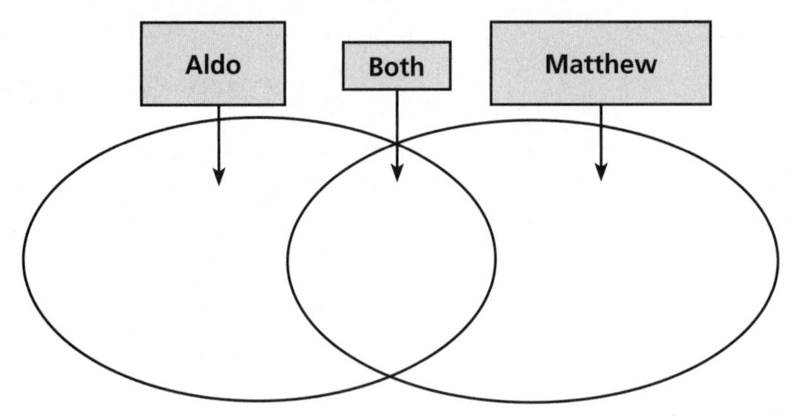

A try to help lonely children
B love to tell stories
C are shy and quiet
D come to the United States from another country

13 How are the situations that Perry and Anne face similar? How are their personalities different? Support your answer with examples from the texts. (5 points)

___

___

___

___

___

___

___

___

Directions: Read the following poem. Then answer the questions that follow.

Secret Treasures

1 They are powerful.
Like a soldier, I'll protect them
From anything that might do them harm.
I hide them,
5 But not underground in some secret place.
I hold them close
Where they are safe,
Cradled beneath my folded arms.
If you are one who can help them grow,
10 I might share them with you.
I'm not selfish; only cautious,
Because they are so real—
They are my dreams, you see; my vision
Of all the things that I can do,
15 Of all that I can be.

14 The second line of the poem reads, "Like a soldier, I'll protect them." This line means that the speaker—

A is a member of the military.
B has a job protecting soldiers.
C will protect his or her dreams, just as a soldier protects his or her country.
D wants to become a soldier in order to protect the country's secret weapons.

15 Which of the following words has nearly the same meaning as the word *cradled* in line 8?

A shoved
B protected
C balanced
D stuffed

16 The ideas in the poem build up to an explanation of the secret treasures in which line?

A line 5
B line 7
C line 12
D line 13

17 The speaker is feeling—

A careful.
B worried.
C dreamy.
D powerful.

18 The theme of the poem is—

A life is short; take risks.
B guard your dreams carefully, and they may come true.
C secrets hurt people.
D the only person you can trust is yourself.

Take a break. Then go on to Part 2.

Mastery Test: Part 2

Estimated time: 50 minutes

Directions: Read the passage and answer the questions that follow.

Choosing the Right Pet

The number of people who own either cats or dogs as pets has grown steadily in recent years. Animal shelters are full of cats and dogs waiting for a home. Potential owners need to think about the advantages and disadvantages of each kind of pet before deciding which fits their needs and lifestyles.

Cats and dogs both provide companionship. Whatever choice they make, pet owners should understand that all cats and dogs require routine veterinary care, a proper diet, and a comfortable place to rest. Both dogs and cats tend to shed their fur, though some shed less than others, so potential pet owners should make sure they don't have allergies or mind those pet hairs on their furniture.

Dogs are pack animals, which means they like to be with others as much as possible. As part of a family's "pack," dogs provide security by warning of approaching strangers. Because many dogs are large and strong, owners must take a good deal of time to train them to be well-behaved members of the pack. Dogs are anxious to please and tend to be easy to train. They especially enjoy training that makes use of their excellent sense of smell, such as tracking or hunting. Most dogs need to be walked at least twice each day, and larger breeds need exercise in addition to their walks.

Cats, on the other hand, are more independent. They don't mind being alone, so cats are a good choice for owners who are not at home much during the day. Cats also do not require as much of an owner's time for training or exercise. Most cats can adapt easily to a small home or apartment and don't need to go outside to get the exercise they need.

19 The article recommends cats to people who are not home a lot. What is one reason that the author gives for this recommendation?

A Cats only need to be walked twice a day.

B Cats can feed themselves.

C Cats do not mind being alone.

D Cats are pack animals.

20 Which of these is an accurate quotation from the passage?

A "Both dogs and cats tend to shed their fur, though some shed more than others."
B "Both dogs and cats tend to shed their fur, some more than others."
C "Dogs and cats tend to shed their fur, though some shed less than others."
D "Both dogs and cats tend to shed their fur. Some shed more than others."

21 Explain the main idea of the second paragraph of the passage. How do the details in this paragraph support the main idea of the article? (3 points)

____
____
____
____
____
____
____
____

Directions: Read the passage and answer the questions that follow.

page 6A | **The Westbury Gazette** | **May 24**

A letter from the editorial board of the newspaper

The arrival of spring brings with it a new beginning. Winter-weary people emerge from their homes, ready to enjoy the outdoors once again. Flowers and plants begin to sprout. And sadly, the Westbury Animal Shelter begins to fill with unwanted and abandoned puppies and kittens. It is difficult not to be moved by the sight of these lonely pets anxiously waiting for a home. Unfortunately, animals that are skittish or fearful have less of a chance of being adopted. These problems are often the result of the animals' fear of the unknown. They have often had little or no experience with people. The best chance for these animals is to "socialize" them by increasing the amount of human contact they have. That is why we applaud the Westbury Animal Shelter's volunteer program. In this program, middle school students become involved with feeding, bathing, and exercising the animals. The students gain a sense of responsibility by caring for the animals. The animals become accustomed to people and new situations. We encourage student volunteers—and volunteers of all ages—to become involved in this win-win situation.

22 What problem does the editorial address?

A People don't get outside enough during the winter.
B Animals who are afraid of people have less chance of being adopted.
C Middle school students have no sense of responsibility.
D People should provide homes for abandoned puppies and kittens.

23 The solution the editorial supports is—

A having students research and report on the problem.
B closing the animal shelter.
C limiting contact with the animals until they are adopted.
D using volunteers to provide human contact for the animals.

24 Which word BEST describes the volunteer program?

A dangerous
B lonely
C valuable
D unwanted

Directions: Use both "Choosing the Right Pet" and the editorial from *The Westbury Gazette* to answer questions 25–28.

25 In both passages, the writers' point of view is that dogs—

A need a responsible owner.
B are so much trouble that people abandon them.
C are not a good choice of pet for middle school kids.
D are a better choice of pet than cats.

26 The structure of "Choosing the Right Pet" is—

A comparison/contrast.
B problem/solution.
C opinion/reasons.
D chronological order.

27 The structure of the newspaper editorial is—

A comparison/contrast.
B problem/solution.
C opinion/reasons.
D chronological order.

28 Why might a young person want to get a puppy as a pet? What could he or she do at the Westbury Animal Shelter to get to know the puppies? Use details from BOTH selections to support your answer. (5 points)

Directions: Read the passage and answer the questions that follow.

Turtles in the Gulf of Mexico

1 Five of the world's seven sea turtle species are found in the Gulf of Mexico: leatherback, hawksbill, green, loggerhead, and Kemp's ridley. These magnificent marine animals, once abundant in the oceans, have declined during the last century. Human development on turtle nesting beaches, harvesting of the eggs, slaughtering for food and consumer products, and incidental capturing by the fishing industry are to blame for dwindling turtle populations.

2 The Kemp's ridley is the most endangered species of sea turtle. Its principal nesting area is a 16-mile stretch of beach at Playa de Rancho Nuevo, Tamaulipas, Mexico, where approximately 40,000 Kemp's ridleys nested in a single day in 1947. Today fewer than 2,000 nest in a year.

3 To save the Kemp's ridley, agencies from the United States Federal Government, the state of Texas, and the Republic of Mexico have joined forces in an attempt to establish a second nesting beach at Padre Island National Seashore, where sporadic Kemp's ridley nesting had already been detected. The program is designed around the theory that mature sea turtles return to the beach where they hatched to then lay their own eggs. Biologists are not yet certain exactly how the turtles recognize a particular beach again. Perhaps they become familiar with the chemical composition of the sand or the seawater, or maybe they know the position of the stars or the sun. It could even have something to do with the Earth's magnetic field, or through other means yet to be discovered.

4 From 1978 to 1988, a total of 22,507 eggs were collected at Rancho Nuevo and placed in Styrofoam boxes containing Padre Island sand. The eggs were then transported to a laboratory at Padre Island National Seashore and incubated. After hatching, the young turtles were released on the beach and allowed to crawl to the surf, hopefully leaving them with a lasting impression of the beach. Following a short swim in the Gulf of Mexico, the baby turtles were recaptured and transported to the National Marine Fisheries Service Laboratory in Galveston, Texas. The turtles were raised for one year in Galveston, growing large enough to avoid most predators and also to be tagged for future recognition. A numbered metal tag was attached to one front flipper of each eight-inch sea turtle. Beginning in 1982, the turtles were also marked with "living tags"—small plugs of their lighter bottom shell implanted into their darker upper shell. Finally, the one-year-old turtles were released permanently into the Gulf of Mexico.

5 In 1996, two Kemp's ridley sea turtles with living tags came ashore and laid eggs at Padre Island National Seashore. These were the first recorded returnees from the 1978–1988 project to establish a second nesting colony here. One of the turtles had been hatched in 1983 and the other in 1986. During 1998, three others from the project were found nesting on South Texas beaches, and, during 1999, another four were located.

6 Since then the numbers have greatly increased. By the end of 2011, preliminary data indicated that over 180 Kemp's ridley sea turtle nests were found on Padre Island. Over 100 of these were on Padre Island Seashore.

29 Which detail should NOT be included in a summary of this selection?

A Efforts have been made to establish new nesting areas for the Kemp's ridley turtle.
B Seven species of sea turtles are found in the Gulf of Mexico.
C Some turtles have begun to nest on Padre Island.
D Scientists worked to familiarize the turtles with Padre Island beaches.

30 What is one reason for the decline of the sea turtle population?

A harvesting of the turtles' eggs
B lack of sand on the beaches
C the turtles' confusion of which beach to go to
D interference with the turtles by scientists

31 Write a summary of "Turtles in the Gulf of Mexico." Include only the main ideas. (3 points)

____

____

____

____

____

32 One main idea in the article is that the Kemp's ridley is the most endangered species of sea turtle. This idea is supported by the fact that—

A 22,507 eggs were collected at Rancho Nuevo beach.
B the Kemp's ridley turtles are marked with "living tags."
C sea turtles are slaughtered for food.
D fewer than 2,000 Kemp's ridley turtles nest per year.

33 Since the prefix *bio-* means life, the word *biologist* means—

A one who studies living things.
B a living thing.
C one who studies turtles.
D a marine animal.

34 The word *population* means—

A the number of people or animals within an area.
B a city or town.
C a beach where turtles live.
D the place where an animal lives.

35 Study the following dictionary entry.

> **principal** *adj.* **1.** most important *n.* **2.** a matter of primary importance **3.** a person with controlling authority **4.** a leading performer or star

Which of the dictionary entries fits the meaning of the word *principal* as it is used in paragraph 2?

A entry 1
B entry 2
C entry 3
D entry 4

Take a break. Then go on to Part 3.

Mastery Test: Part 3

Estimated time: 15 minutes

Directions: Choose the best answer for the following questions.

36 In which sentence is the underlined word NOT spelled correctly?

A Mom couldn't make cookies because she was out of flour.
B My brother's toy car is made of metal.
C We red a poem called "The Road Not Taken."
D I got a new pair of gloves to go with my ski jacket.

37 What part of speech is the underlined word in the sentence below?

Juan cried, "No! Don't drop the book on my model!"

A verb
B adjective
C preposition
D interjection

38 Choose the correct verb tense for the following sentence.

By the time the contest ended, more than one hundred students ______ their art.

A entered
B enters
C will enter
D had entered

39 Which sentence is punctuated correctly?

A For dinner I ate rice, beans, and fish.
B Amy, my closest neighbor knows how to do the hula.
C My mom likes to golf, Dad would rather sit by the pool.
D "Today is my favorite day" said Ellen.

40 In which sentence is the underlined word NOT spelled correctly?

A She asked me to pause after I read the last line of the poem.
B Some gum is stuck to the sole of my shoe.
C Tim ate almost the whole cake.
D We past two people on bicycles.

GO ON

41 Identify the conjunction in the following sentence.

If we don't see any stars, we can just sit and talk for a while.

A If
B stars
C and
D for

42 Choose the correct verb tense for the following sentence.

My dad ______ kindergarten since 1992.

A has taught
B teaches
C will teach
D taught

43 Which of the following titles is correctly punctuated?

A My grandmother's favorite song is *Amazing Grace.*
B Have you read the book *The Phantom Tollbooth*?
C I learned how to build a fire by reading "Boy's Life" magazine.
D The article was called, How to Survive in the Woods.

44 Which of the following is correctly punctuated?

A Maya, will you please read me a story?
B It's your turn to take out the trash; isn't it?
C If I'm not home after school I'm at the YMCA.
D I enjoy playing football but, I'm not a fan of soccer.

45 Which of the following sentences is NOT correctly punctuated?

A Yolanda, Jack, Ahmir, and I went to the *Titanic* exhibit.
B We saw how the ship was constructed, what life was like on board, and how the ship sank.
C The following items were recovered from the ocean floor: dishes, jewelry, and other personal items.
D The exhibit will stop in Las Vegas, Nevada: Greensboro, South Carolina: and Tallahassee, Florida.

46 Choose the correct verb tense for the following sentence.

After I finished my homework, I ______ my bike.

A ride
B rode
C will ride
D have ridden

Directions: Read the following paragraph. Then answer the questions that follow.

[1]As a young man, John Muir used his curious mind to invent unusual objects. [2]One unique invention was a thermometer sensitive enough to react to a person's body heat from several feet away. [3]Muir also designed an alarm clock that tipped the bed and dumped the sleeper on the floor. [4]However, Muir's greatest love was for the outdoors, so he is better remembered for his work as a naturalist. [5]He is also remembered as a conservationist. [6]He explored and wrote about the wilderness in places such as California and Alaska. [7]In 1872, Muir founded the Sierra Club, an organization that still works to conserve America's wilderness areas.

47 Combine sentences 4 and 5 into one sentence using the correlative conjunctions *both / and.* (1 point)

____

____

____

48 All of the following are prepositional phrases EXCEPT—

A *on the floor.*
B *about the wilderness.*
C *for his work.*
D *was a thermometer.*

49 The prefix *un-* as used in the word unusual means—

A under.
B again.
C not.
D more than.

GO ON

50 Which word has the same root word as <u>naturalist</u>?

A nature
B number
C naughty
D turn

51 Based upon the context, a <u>conservationist</u> is someone who—

A saves energy.
B protects nature.
C invents new things.
D is very curious.

52 An antonym for <u>conserve</u> is—

A protect.
B destroy.
C explore.
D build.

Points Earned/Total = ______/70

Keeping Score

	Points Earned / Total Points	Percent Score
Tryout Test	/70	%
Unit One Practice Test Reading Literature: Key Ideas and Details	/10	%
Unit Two Practice Test Reading Literature: Craft and Structure	/8	%
Unit Three Practice Test Reading Informational Text: Key Ideas and Details	/10	%
Unit Four Practice Test Reading Informational Text: Craft and Structure	/12	%
Unit Five Practice Test Language: Grammar and Usage	/10	%
Unit Six Practice Test Language: Capitalization, Punctuation, and Spelling	/8	%
Unit Seven Practice Test Language: Vocabulary	/10	%
Mastery Test	/70	%

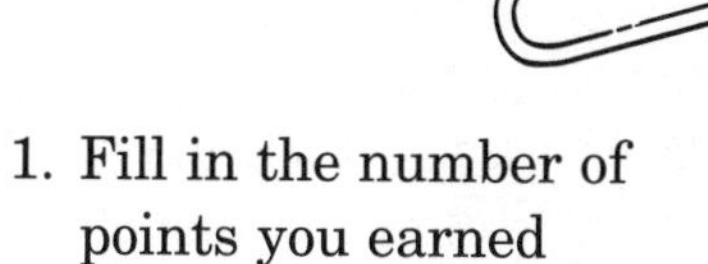

1. Fill in the number of points you earned in the Points Earned box.
2. Use the Finding Percent chart on page 128 to figure out your Percent Score. Then fill in the % box.
3. Compare your Percent Scores for the Tryout Test and the Mastery Test. See how much you've learned!

Finding Percent

Many tests give your score in both number of points earned and in percentages. This handy chart will tell you your percent score.

1. Find the band with the same number of points that are on your test.
2. Follow along the top row of the band to the number of points you earned. Your percent score is right below it.

Number of Points on Test

8	1	2	3	4	5	6	7	8
	13%	25%	38%	50%	63%	75%	88%	100%

10	1	2	3	4	5	6	7	8	9	10
	10%	20%	30%	40%	50%	60%	70%	80%	90%	100%

12	1	2	3	4	5	6	7	8	9	10	11	12
	8%	17%	25%	33%	42%	50%	58%	67%	75%	83%	92%	100%

70	1	2	3	4	5	6	7	8	9	10	11	12	13	14	15	16	17
	1%	3%	4%	6%	7%	9%	10%	11%	13%	14%	16%	17%	19%	20%	21%	23%	24%
	18	19	20	21	22	23	24	25	26	27	28	29	30	31	32	33	34
	26%	27%	29%	30%	31%	33%	34%	36%	37%	39%	40%	41%	43%	44%	46%	47%	49%
	35	36	37	38	39	40	41	42	43	44	45	46	47	48	49	50	51
	50%	51%	53%	54%	56%	57%	59%	60%	61%	63%	64%	66%	67%	69%	70%	71%	73%
	52	53	54	55	56	57	58	59	60	61	62	63	64	65	66	67	68
	74%	76%	77%	79%	80%	81%	83%	84%	86%	87%	89%	90%	91%	93%	94%	96%	97%
	69	70															
	99%	100%															

WRITING TEST WORKSHOPS

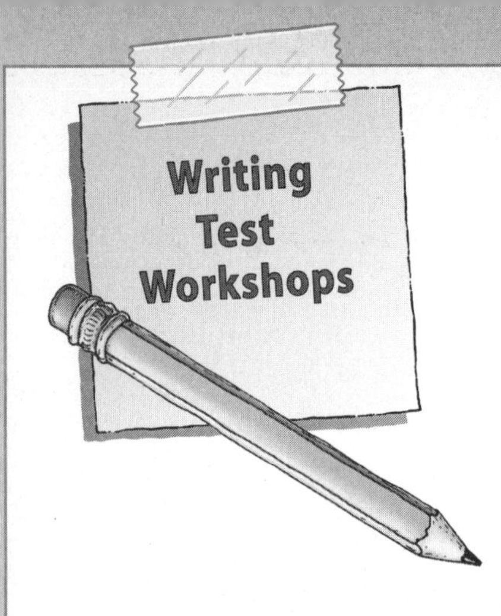

To the Student

Why Do I Need This Book?

This book will help you practice taking writing tests. You will learn how to—

- read a writing prompt.
- get your ideas down on paper.
- write to tell a story.
- write to explain.
- write about an opinion.

How Will My Writing Be Scored?

Your writing test will be scored by test readers who use rubrics, or scoring guides. The rubric below lists 6 qualities of good writing. Read through each characteristic so you know how your writing will be graded.

Rubric Score: *1* is the lowest; *5* is the highest					
Ideas/Content—focuses on one main idea; the details add to the main idea	①	②	③	④	⑤
Organization—has a clear beginning, middle, and end; the order is easy to follow	①	②	③	④	⑤
Voice—communicates feelings and personality; the writing is unique	①	②	③	④	⑤
Word Choice—uses colorful, fresh words in the right places	①	②	③	④	⑤
Sentence Fluency—uses both long and short sentences that flow smoothly	①	②	③	④	⑤
Conventions—has few or no spelling, capitalization, and punctuation errors	①	②	③	④	⑤

How to Manage Your Time During an Essay Test

You may have 20 to 45 minutes to complete a writing test so it's important to have a plan.

If you have 20 minutes,

- read the prompt, circle key ideas, brainstorm, and organize ideas (5 minutes)
- write the essay (10 minutes)
- revise, edit, and proofread (5 minutes)

How to Read a Writing Prompt

A *prompt* is the assignment for a writing test. The prompt gives you directions. It also tells you what to write about.

◎ **Step 1**

Read through the entire prompt. Decide what the topic is.

◎ **Step 2**

Read through the prompt a second time, underlining key words (*explain, compare, tell*) that will help you focus your writing.

◎ **Step 3**

Look for key words or phrases you might use in your main idea statement.

Ty's Prompt

Here is a prompt for Ty's test. Look at the key words he underlined. They helped Ty understand exactly what he was supposed to do.

Prompt

The city council is thinking about passing a new law. It would <u>ban the use of bikes, in-line skates, and skateboards on public sidewalks</u>. <u>Decide how you feel</u> about this idea. Then <u>write about your opinion</u>. <u>Support your opinion with convincing reasons</u>. Be sure to <u>explain your reasons in detail</u>.

From the prompt, Ty will have to write about his opinion on the new law. His paper must include reasons that he will explain in detail.

Try It

Directions: Read the prompt below. Underline the key words or phrases that might be helpful to a writer.

Prompt

People live in rural areas, small or large towns, or big cities. Think about where you live or places you have visited. Choose one place where you would like to live. Explain why you think it is best. Be sure to give specific details.

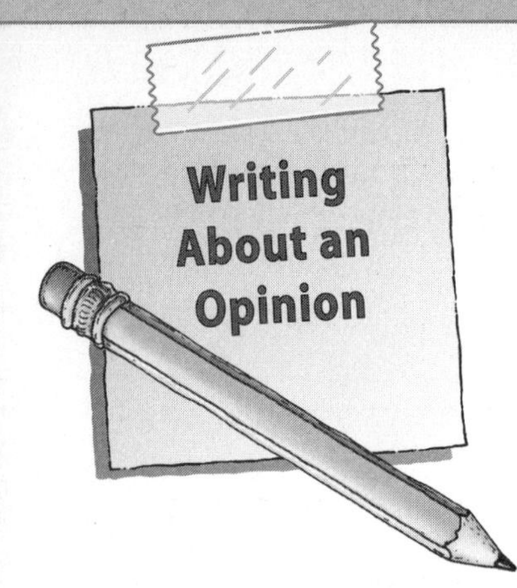

Writing About an Opinion

Review the Standards (W.5.1.a–d, W.5.4, W.5.5, L.5.3.b)

- Write an **opinion** piece, supporting a **point of view** with **reasons**
- Include an **introduction** and a **conclusion**
- Support reasons with **facts** and **details**
- Use **linking words** and **phrases**

Some writing tests will ask you to write about an **opinion**. This is also called *persuasive writing*. When writing about an opinion, you must explain your **point of view** and then give **reasons** in support of your opinion. Your paper should have three parts.

Introduction

- introduces the topic
- states your opinion (main idea) in one sentence

Opinion Statment: *I am in favor of year-round school.*

Body

- has one or more paragraphs
- gives reasons supporting your opinion
- includes **facts** and **details** to explain your reasons

Reason: *Kids forget the things they've learned over the summer.*

Facts/Details: *Teachers spend most of September reviewing things the kids learned the year before. This is a waste of time and money.*

The best reasons—

- involve safety or health issues
- involve spending money
- affect the most people

Facts and details might include—

- personal stories
- opinions from experts
- examples

Conclusion

- restates your opinion
- ends with a strong thought

Example: *Year-round school is a smart move for teachers, parents, and kids!*

Try It

Directions: On the lines below, write another reason to support the opinion: *I am in favor of year-round school.* Then write some facts or details to support your opinion.

Reason ____

____

Facts/Details ____

____

Erin's Prompt

Below is a prompt Erin was given on a writing test. Help her out by underlining the key words for her.

Prompt

Your local school board is thinking about making students wear uniforms. The board members have asked for the opinion of all students before making a decision. Write a paper presenting your opinion to the school board members. Support your opinion with good reasons.

Before writing her paper, Erin used a chart to help her organize her ideas. Notice that she placed her main idea at the top of the organizer. Then she listed her supporting reasons. Finally, she placed a star by the reasons she thought were most important.

Words used in opinion writing prompts

- agree/disagree
- argue/argument
- convince
- oppose
- persuade
- point of view/viewpoint
- position
- support

Topic: Wearing School Uniforms **My Opinion/Point of View:** I am in favor of school uniforms.
Reasons
* less expensive than brand-name clothing
uniforms would be "cool" if designed right
* would be more presentable
* would save time choosing what to wear
would help school officials recognize people who don't belong at school

Directions: Read Erin's paper. Then complete the tasks in the Looking at Erin's Paper boxes.

School Uniforms

Do you pay attention to what others wear? Do you wish you had clothes like theirs? Many students do. That's why I think wearing uniforms to school is a good idea.

I understand that some people feel that wearing school uniforms doesn't allow students to express themselves. Others think that everyone would look the same if they wore uniforms.

However, I feel that wearing school uniforms would solve a number of problems that occur in schools every day. Having school uniforms would stop those problems that occur when students don't have enough money to buy brand-name clothing. How many times have you heard parents complain about the price of clothing? Mine do all the time. Brand-name clothes are expensive. But many students think they are the only "cool" stuff to wear. Some students are teased because they don't have brand-name clothes.

Looking at Erin's Paper

- Does Erin's introduction grab your attention? Why or why not?
- Underline Erin's central idea. Is her opinion on wearing school uniforms clearly stated?
- Does Erin include her strongest reasons for wearing uniforms? (See chart on page 133.) If not, what reason or reasons might she have included? Why?
- Write *Detail* next to sentences in the third paragraph that contain details in support of a reason.

School uniforms could help in other ways too. They would look more presentable than some of the T-shirts students wear. If everyone wore school uniforms, teachers wouldn't have to send students home or be embarrassed when a visitor comes to class.

Uniforms could change a lot of people's lives. Each morning, many students have a hard time finding the right clothes to wear. They don't want to be teased if they wear the wrong outfit. Or they don't want to be embarrassed because their clothes are old and out of style. I would rather wear the same outfit every day than waste time every morning choosing clothes. I could use this time for chores, extra studying, or reading.

I believe that the school board should decide to have students wear uniforms. Teachers and parents would be happier. And in the long run, students would be happier too.

Looking at Erin's Paper

- Circle places where Erin uses strong nouns and verbs.
- Underline places where Erin uses weak or confusing words.
- Does Erin restate her opinion in the conclusion? If so, underline her opinion and mark it with an **O** for opinion statement.
- Erin's final sentence is weak. On the lines below the paper, rewrite her final sentence so that it packs more punch.

____

____

____

Try It On Your Own

Now it's your turn to take a practice writing test. Follow the steps in order. If your teacher gives you a time limit, make a plan by filling in the amount of minutes you have to complete each step.

_____ minutes

Step 1—Read the prompt carefully. Underline any key words. (_____ minutes)
Step 2—Brainstorm for some ideas on another piece of paper. (_____ minutes)
Step 3—Fill in the organizer with your ideas. (_____ minutes)

Prompt

Some school districts in the United States feel that boys and girls are not treated equally in all subject areas. Therefore, they have created all-boy and all-girl classes in elementary schools. Think about the issue, and then write a paper that states your opinion about whether having all-boy and all-girl classes is a good or bad idea. Support your opinion with clear reasons.

Topic: ____________________

Opinion Statement/Point of View: ____________________

Reasons

1. ____________________

2. ____________________

3. ____________________

Step 4—Using your organizer as a guide, write your paper on a separate piece of paper. (______ minutes)

Step 5—Go back and revise your paper. Then proofread for mistakes in capitalization, punctuation, and grammar. (______ minutes)

How Did You Do?

Directions: Now evaluate your own writing (or ask a friend). Complete the following steps.

Consider This

1. **Ideas/Content** Underline your opinion statement.
   - Number the reasons that support your position statement.
   - Put a check mark by your strongest reason.
2. **Organization** Can you identify the introduction and conclusion? Write **I** and **C** next to them.
   - Put a box around linking words such as *first, next, second, finally,* and *also.*
3. **Voice** Does the writing communicate a positive attitude, or does it seem angry or sound like a know-it-all?
4. **Word Choice** Circle any words that seem especially fresh or vivid. Cross out any words that are not exciting or precise.
5. **Sentence Fluency** Put a check next to any sentences that seem too choppy or too long. Try combining sentences that are too short or creating two sentences from an overly long one.
6. **Conventions** Check for any errors in spelling, capitalization, and punctuation.

Use your answers from the **Consider This** chart to help you fill in this rubric.

Rubric Score: *1* is the lowest; *5* is the highest					
Ideas/Content—focuses on one main idea; the details add to the main idea	①	②	③	④	⑤
Organization—has a clear beginning, middle, and end; the order is easy to follow	①	②	③	④	⑤
Voice—communicates feelings and personality; the writing is unique	①	②	③	④	⑤
Word Choice—uses colorful, fresh words in the right places	①	②	③	④	⑤
Sentence Fluency—uses both long and short sentences that flow smoothly	①	②	③	④	⑤
Conventions—has few or no spelling, capitalization, and punctuation errors	①	②	③	④	⑤

One way I can improve my writing is by ____

____

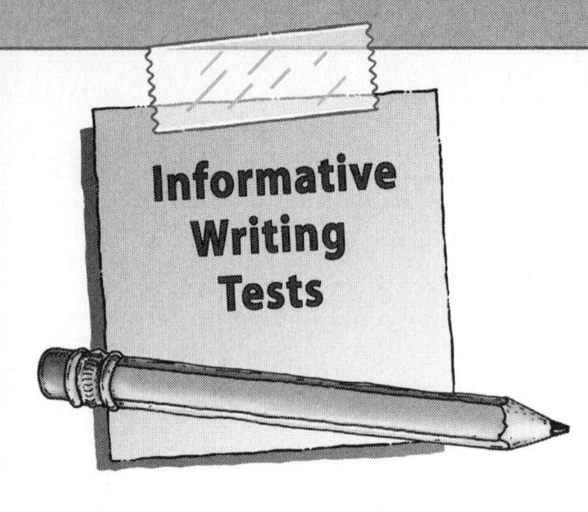

Writing to Inform

Review the Standards (W.5.2.a–e, W.5.4, W.5.5, L.5.2)

- Write **informative** texts with an **introduction** and a **conclusion**
- Develop the main idea using **facts**, **definitions**, and **examples**
- Use precise language and **linking words**

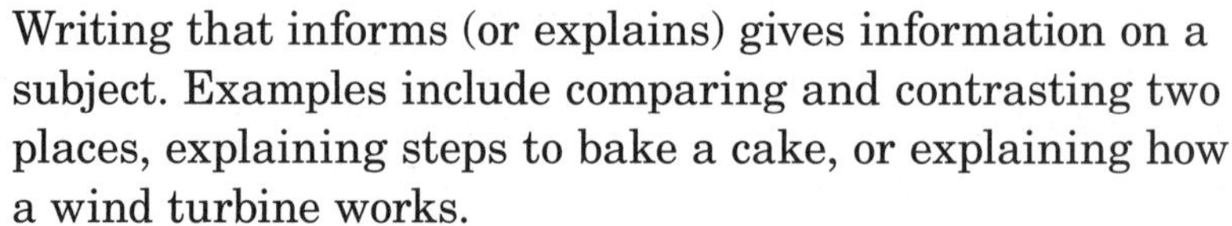

Writing that informs (or explains) gives information on a subject. Examples include comparing and contrasting two places, explaining steps to bake a cake, or explaining how a wind turbine works.

An **informative** paper has three parts:

Introduction

- gets the reader's attention
- presents the main idea statement

Main Idea: *Farming is an interesting occupation.*

"Hook" your reader by—

- giving a surprising fact
- telling them a story
- asking a question

Body

- contains one or more paragraphs
- uses good **linking words** between ideas
- supports the main idea by giving details, **examples**, **facts**, **definitions**, or quotations

Examples of Supporting Details:

Farmers work with animals.

Farmers get to work outdoors.

Farmers also have to be good businesspeople.

Use linking words to help the reader follow the ideas in your paper: *first, later, next, another, because, however, after, also, for example*

Conclusion

- sums up the paper
- contains a strong concluding thought

Concluding thought: *A farmer must have many talents to be successful. It is definitely an interesting job.*

Kelsie's Prompt

Below is a prompt Kelsie was given on a writing test. Help her out by underlining the key words for her.

Words used in informative writing prompts

- compare/contrast
- define
- explain
- summarize
- tell

Prompt

Many children in America are unhealthy. They don't eat right or get enough exercise. Explain some things a child your age should do to be strong and healthy.

Before writing her paper, Kelsie used an idea web to help her organize her ideas.

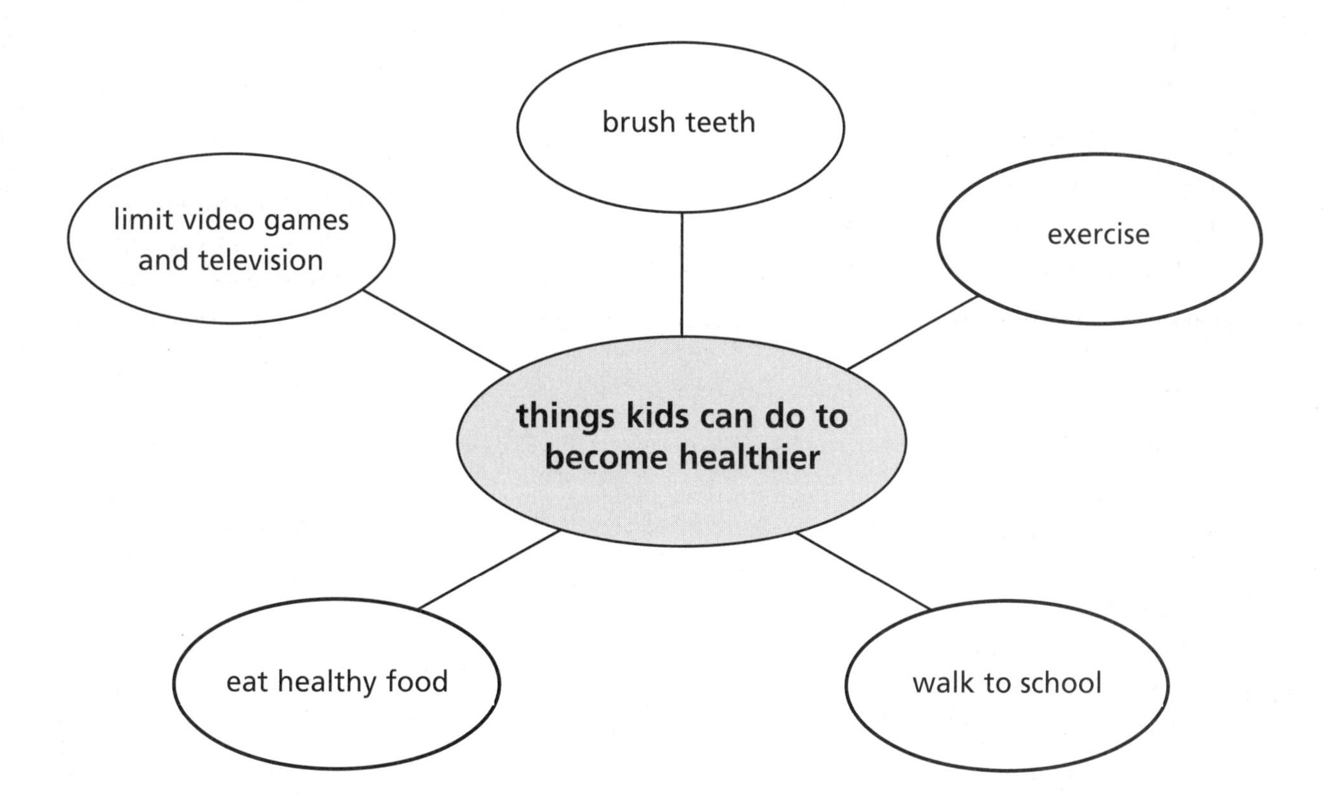

Directions: Read Kelsie's paper. Then complete the tasks in the Looking at Kelsie's Paper box.

Healthier, Happier Kids

Did you know that more and more kids are obese? Kids these days are fat and lazy because of all the video games and stuff. Even Michelle Obama has been on TV trying to get kids to eat healthier and exercise more. There are some easy things that kids can do to become healthier.

First, kids need more exercise to be healthy. Doctors say that kids should exercise for 60 minutes every day. Not just walking from the couch to the refrigerator, but running, riding bikes, or playing soccer. My soccer team is the Comets. Find something active you enjoy doing. It might be riding your bike, playing on a basketball team, or jump on a trampoline. Just get off the couch and get going!

Kids need to eat healthier. Often at lunch I see kid's eating candy, cookies, and potato chips. These foods contain a lot of sugar and not many vitamins and minerals. Fruits and raw vegetables are delicious. Try packing them in your lunch instead of food that may taste good but leaves you feeling tired.

These are just a few things kids can do to become healthier. Why not challenge a friend to try some of these things and see how much better you'll feel.

Looking at Kelsie's Paper

1. Underline the main idea. Number the supporting details with 1 and 2.
2. Where does Kelsie's voice become too harsh? Cross out and change the inappropriate words.
3. Does the essay have a clear beginning, middle, and end? Yes ___ No ____
4. Put stars by two facts Kelsie includes in her paper.
5. Cross out any sentences that don't fit with the main idea of the paragraph.
6. Cross out and change any words that could be more precise.
7. Circle a linking word. Add a linking word to the third paragraph.
8. Fix one sentence fragment.
9. Add another sentence to the conclusion to make the ending stronger.
10. Mark and correct any errors in mechanics, punctuation, and spelling.

Try It On Your Own

Now it's your turn to take a practice writing test. Follow the steps in order. If your teacher gives you a time limit, make a plan by filling in the amount of minutes you have to complete each step.

_____ minutes

Step 1—Read the prompt below. Underline the key words that will guide your writing. (_____ minutes)

Step 2—Brainstorm for some ideas on another piece of paper. (_____ minutes)

Step 3—Fill in the idea web with your ideas. (_____ minutes)

Prompt

Almost everyone has jobs or chores, whether it's walking the dog or taking out the garbage. Explain what your job or chore is. Include how and why you do it.

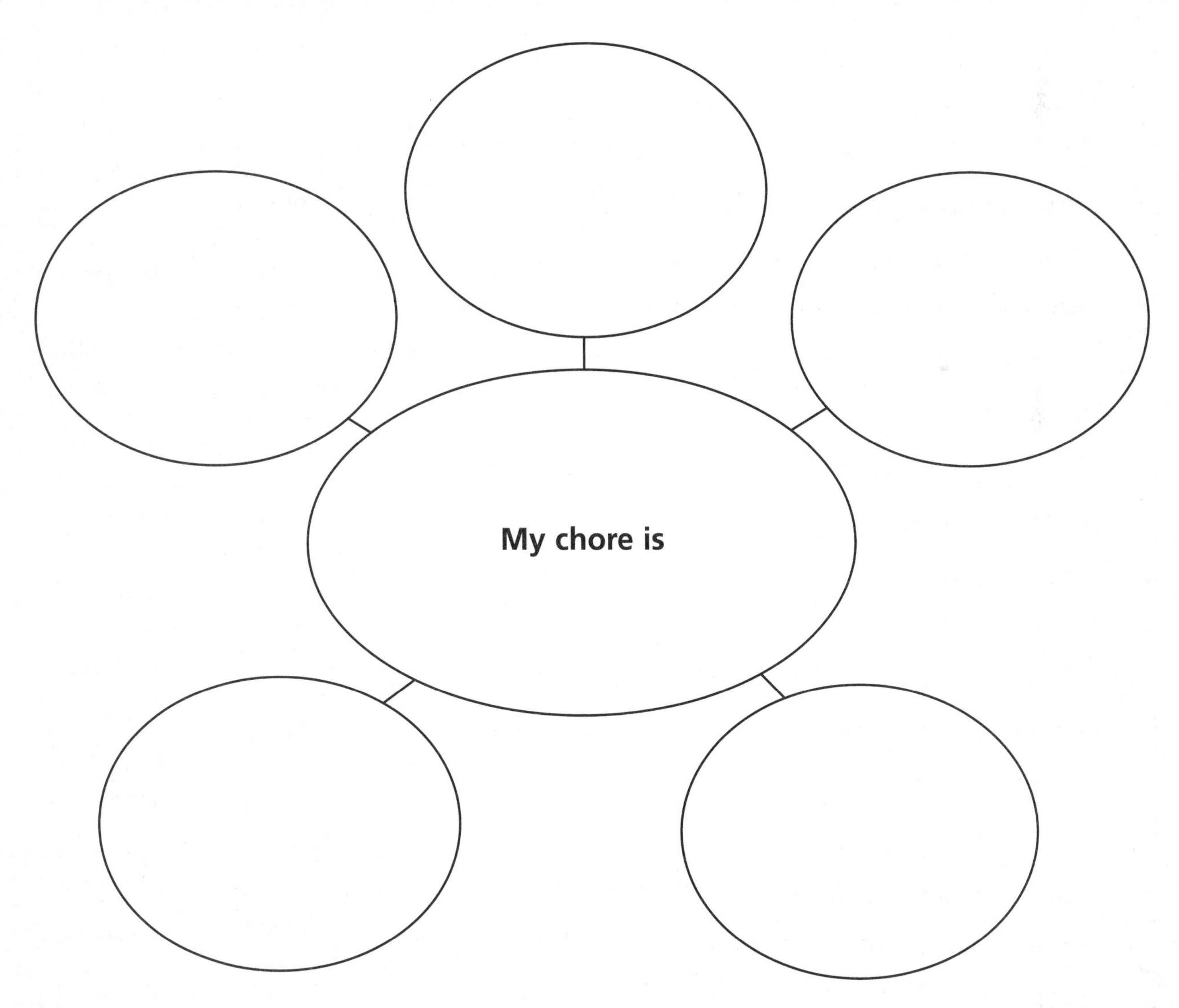

GO ON

Step 4—Using your idea web as a guide, write your essay on a separate piece of paper. (_____ minutes)

Step 5—Go back and revise your paper. Then proofread for mistakes in capitalization, punctuation, and grammar. (_____ minutes)

How Did You Do?

Directions: Now evaluate your own writing (or ask a friend). Complete the following steps.

Consider This

1. **Ideas/Content** Underline your main idea statement.
   - Number the supporting details that support your main idea.
2. **Organization** Can you identify the introduction and conclusion? Write **I** and **C** next to them.
   - Put a box around linking words such as *first, next, second, finally,* and *also.*
3. **Voice** Does the writing communicate a positive, confident attitude? Put a **V** next to any parts that seem too negative or not confident.
4. **Word Choice** Circle any words that seem especially fresh or vivid. Cross out any words that are boring or not precise.
5. **Sentence Fluency** Put a check next to any sentences that seem too choppy or too long.
6. **Conventions** Check for any errors in spelling, capitalization, and punctuation.

Use your answers from the **Consider This** chart to help you fill in this rubric.

Rubric Score: *1* is the lowest; *5* is the highest					
Ideas/Content—focuses on one main idea; the details add to the main idea	①	②	③	④	⑤
Organization—has a clear beginning, middle, and end; the order is easy to follow	①	②	③	④	⑤
Voice—communicates feelings and personality; the writing is unique	①	②	③	④	⑤
Word Choice—uses colorful, fresh words in the right places	①	②	③	④	⑤
Sentence Fluency—uses both long and short sentences that flow smoothly	①	②	③	④	⑤
Conventions—has few or no spelling, capitalization, and punctuation errors	①	②	③	④	⑤

One way I can improve my writing is by ______________________________

____

____

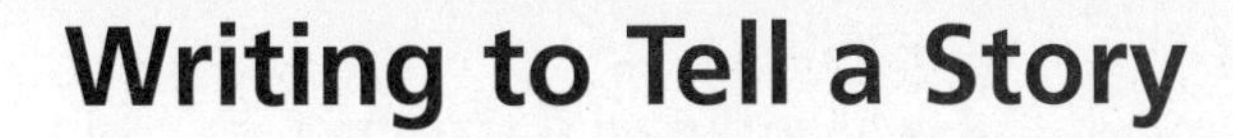

Writing to Tell a Story

Review the Standards (W.5.3.a–e, W.5.4, W.5.5)

- Write **narratives** about real or imagined experiences
- Explain a **situation**, **characters**, and **events**
- Use **dialogue** and **description**
- Use **transitional words**
- Choose words and phrases to convey ideas precisely
- Provide a **conclusion**

When you tell a story, you are **narrating** events. (That's why telling a story is called *narrative writing.*) The events you are describing may have really happened to you, or they may be made up. A narrative has the following parts.

Beginning

- introduces **characters** and a **situation** (a problem or conflict)
- describes the setting (when and where the story takes place)
- may include a main idea statement, for example: *I'll never forget my tenth birthday party.*

Middle

- contains the main **events** of your story that build by developing the problem or conflict
- uses **transitional words** such as *next, then, when, after, later*
- Uses **dialogue** and **description**

"What's **dialogue**?" Joey asked.

"It's talking between characters," Mia replied.

Joey said with a laugh, "Oh, like what we're doing right now!"

Description—precise, lively words

"The sky turned grey as I pedaled my bike toward my house."

Ending

- provides a **conclusion** by explaining how the problem or conflict ends
- may tell what the characters learned:

Although Travis enjoyed his adventure, he was glad to be back home in his own bed.

or how the events changed you:

After being in the school play, I have never again been afraid to speak in front of people.

K.J.'s Prompt

Below is a prompt K.J. was given on a writing test. Help him out by underlining the key words for him.

Words you might find in a narrative writing prompt

experience   define
story   tell
time   narrate
recall

Prompt

Pretend that you and a friend found a map that shows where a treasure is buried. Write a story telling about the adventure you and your friend had trying to find the treasure.

Before writing his paper, K.J. used a story map to help him organize his ideas.

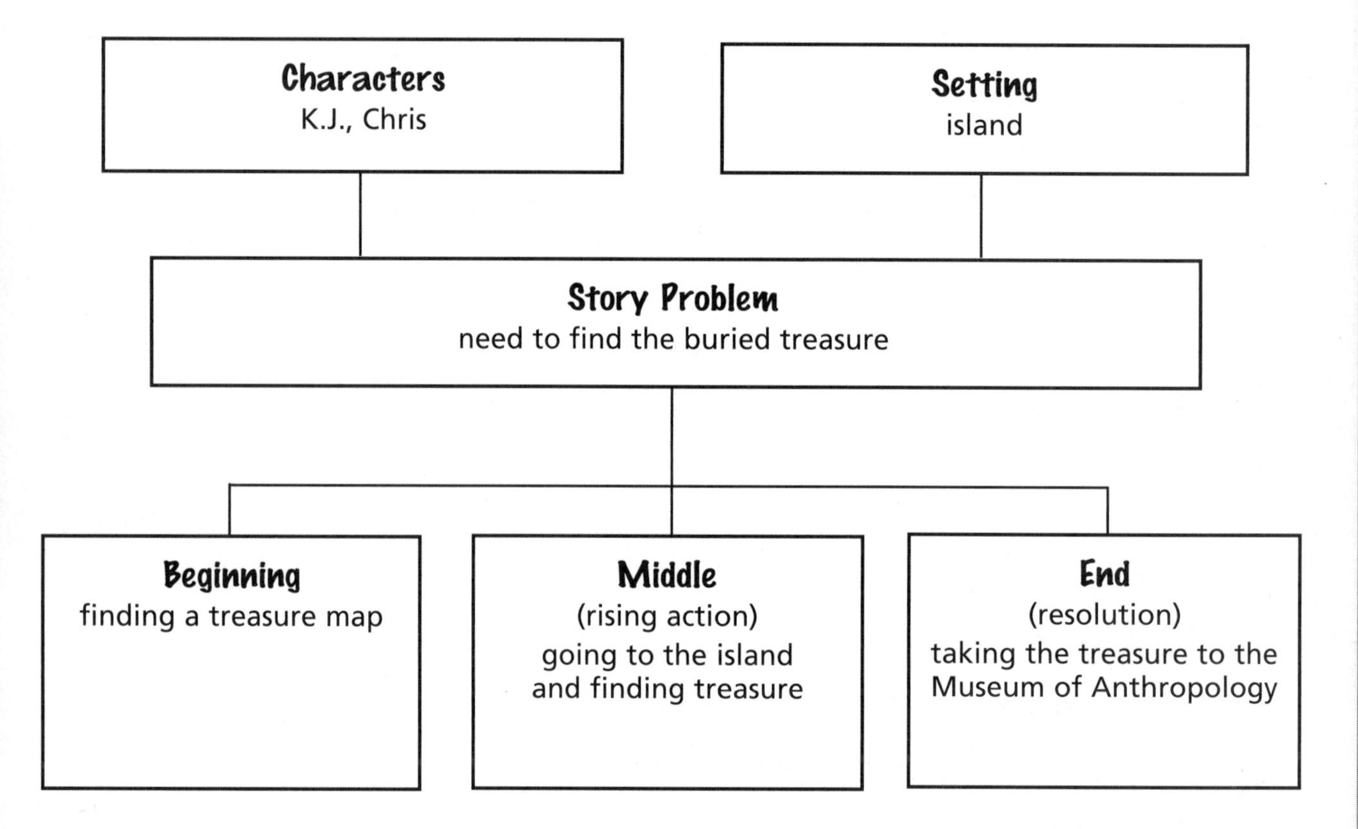

Directions: Read K.J.'s paper. Then complete the tasks in the Looking at K.J.'s Paper box.

Blackbeard's Treasure

It all happened last year during fourth grade. One day after school, Chris and I were playing down at Witchacha Park. We were swinging and decided to go down the slide. So we jumped off our swings and started across the playground. Then, for no apparent reason, Chris tripped on something. It was a little metal box. It was buried in the sand, so we dug it up. Carefully folded inside was a treasure map. We unfolded it and looked at it.

"How are we going to get to the island?" asked Chris.

"There is a rowboat right there," I said, pointing to the map. "But first we need to go home and get some shovels to dig up the treasure."

When we got back, we put the shovels in the boat and pushed off. We reached the island in no time.

"It's 4:30, and I'm hungry," Chris whined.

"First let's dig up the treasure. Then we'll go back to my house and grab a bite to eat."

The map showed that there were two palm trees on the island. The treasure was buried between them. After two long hours of digging, there was a clank! We looked at each other.

Finally, Chris said, "It will take us at least an

Looking at K.J.'s Paper

- Does K.J.'s opening grab your attention? Why or why not?
- Who are the main characters?
- What is the main problem of the story?

hour to get the treasure out of this hole. Won't our parents be getting worried?"

"No, because they went out to eat together," I assured him.

After an hour, we got the treasure out of the hole. We opened the big metal box. Our mouths fell open as we stared at the treasure.

Inside the box were gold coins, garnets, amethysts, bloodstones, and diamonds. There were also emeralds, pearls, rubies, sardonyxes, sapphires, opals, topazes, and turquoises. On top of the treasure, we saw a note. It read:

Congratulations! You have found the treasure of Captain Blackbeard. If you find my other treasures, you'll be sorry! I'll let this one go.
Captain Blackbeard

"That note gives me the creeps," Chris said.

"Me too," I answered.

Two weeks later, we took the treasure and gave it to the Museum of Anthropology. They offered us a one-billion-dollar reward!

Chris and I looked at each other, shrugged our shoulders, and said, "Sure!"

We donated the money to churches, schools, and charities. The museum asked us to tell our story. We told them it was a long story, but they didn't seem to mind.

"It all happened last year in fourth grade. Chris and I . . . "

Looking at K.J.'s Story

- Circle any event in K.J.'s story that does not tie into the main problem.
- Does K.J.'s ending resolve the main problem of the story? Explain your answer.

Try It On Your Own

Now it's your turn to take a practice writing test. Follow the steps in order. If your teacher gives you a time limit, make a plan by filling in the amount of time you have to complete each step.

Time Allowed

_____ minutes

Step 1—Read the prompt below. Underline the key words that will help guide your writing. (_____ minutes)
Step 2—Brainstorm for some ideas on another piece of paper. (_____ minutes)
Step 3—Fill in the story map with your ideas. (_____ minutes)

Prompt

Imagine that your favorite fictional character has come to life for a day and is visiting your school. Write a story about one of his or her experiences.

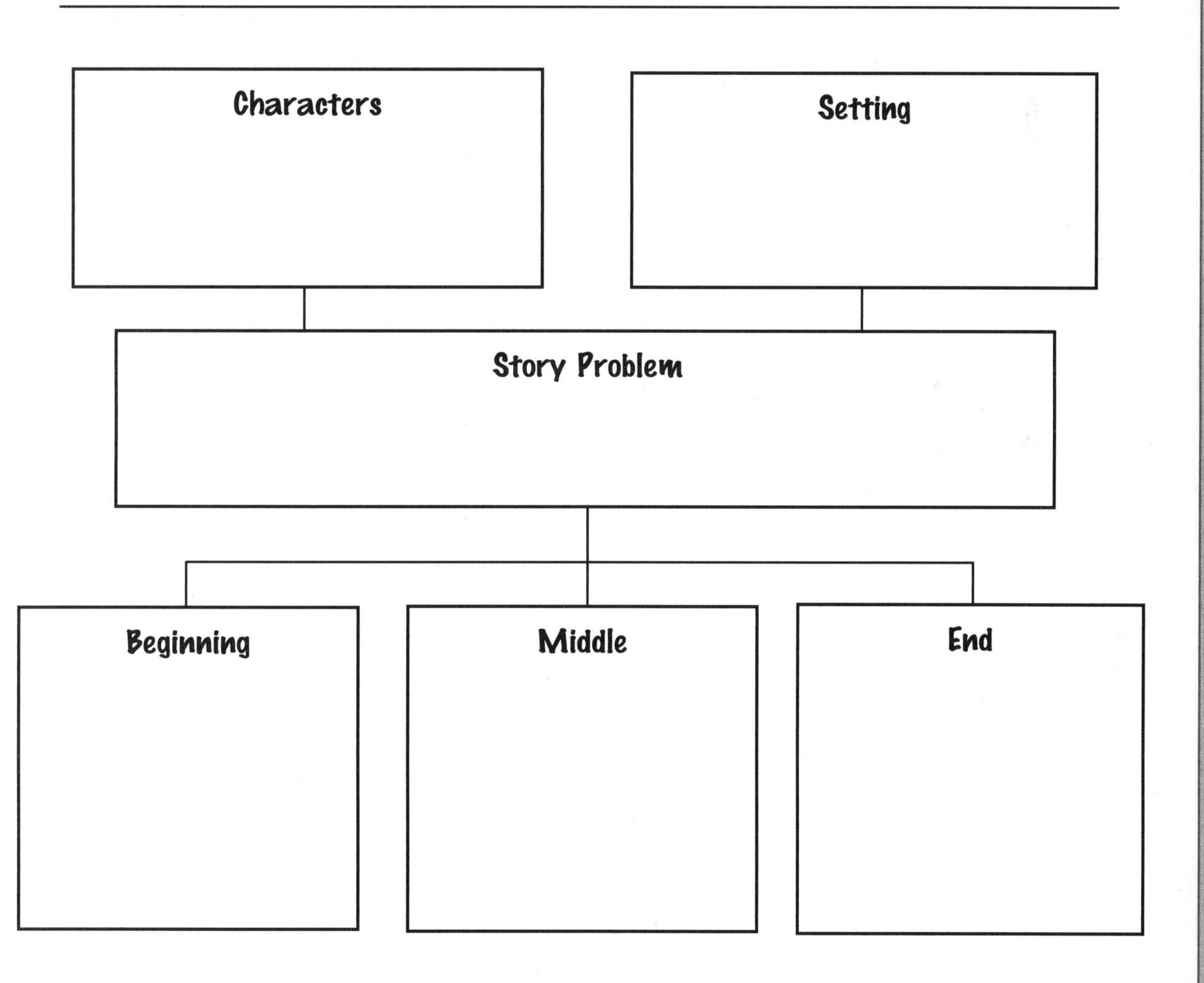

Step 4—Using your story map as a guide, write your story on a separate piece of paper. (_____ minutes)

Step 5—Go back and revise your paper. Then proofread for mistakes in capitalization, punctuation, and grammar. (_____ minutes)

How Did You Do?

Directions: Now evaluate your own writing (or ask a friend). Complete the following steps.

Consider This

1. **Ideas/Content** Underline the sentence that contains the main problem or conflict in the story.
   - Put a check by any events that stray away from the main problem.
   - Put a smiley face next to good description or dialogue.
2. **Organization** Identify the beginning, middle, and ending of the story by writing **B**, **M**, and **E** next to where you find them in the story.
   - Put a box around linking words such as *later, next, then,* and *after.*
3. **Voice** Put a **V** next to any part of the story where the writer's voice doesn't fit or seems strange.
4. **Word Choice** Circle any words that seem especially fresh or vivid. Cross out any words that are boring or not precise.
5. **Sentence Fluency** Put a check next to any sentences that seem too choppy or too long.
6. **Conventions** Check for any errors in spelling, capitalization, and punctuation.

Use your answers from the **Consider This** chart to help you fill in this rubric.

Rubric Score: *1* is the lowest; *5* is the highest					
Ideas/Content—focuses on one main idea; the details add to the main idea	①	②	③	④	⑤
Organization—has a clear beginning, middle, and end; the order is easy to follow	①	②	③	④	⑤
Voice—communicates feelings and personality; the writing is unique	①	②	③	④	⑤
Word Choice—uses colorful, fresh words in the right places	①	②	③	④	⑤
Sentence Fluency—uses both long and short sentences that flow smoothly	①	②	③	④	⑤
Conventions—has few or no spelling, capitalization, and punctuation errors	①	②	③	④	⑤

One way I can improve my writing is by ____

____